Foreword

This report has had a long genesis. It began life in 2004 as a supplementary report to the Manchester Business School (MBS) evaluation of the Six Sigma training programme run by the NHS Mod[...]

The report wa[...]  [...] here were discussions ab[...] [...] no got access to it enthusec [...] Library Services [...] e principles and approach [...] [...] d spread. Eventually, th[...] **This item must be returned** [...] [...] icial paper that the NHS Instit [...] **another borrower, o[...]** [...] to review and update the paper for publication and w[...]

The timing of publication is for[...] , just after Lord Darzi's report from the Next Stage Review of the NHS, *High Quality Care for All*. The Next Stage Review gives a significant and welcome prominence to quality improvement in the next stage of NHS reform. It also sets out, in chapter five, the "core elements of any approach to leadership". These include method: "the management method (leaders) will use for implementation, continuous improvement and measuring success".

Quality healthcare is dependent on method. Each of us, whether commissioner or provider, needs to develop skills and knowledge in methods for improvement. The authors of this report have summarised the improvement approaches and methods that have been successfully utilised by industry over the past 50 years. They have evaluated all the approaches from a healthcare perspective. They have assessed the full spectrum, from the previous favourites such as Total Quality Management and Re-engineering, to current preferences like Lean and Six Sigma to concepts such as Mass Customisation that are newly emerging from the international healthcare improvement movement.

There are some key messages for NHS leaders in this report. Firstly, when we treat clinically-led improvement (audit, clinical governance, etc) as a separate entity from managerially-led performance improvement, we do so at our peril. Leading organisations in healthcare quality have aligned improvement objectives and operate with a definition of quality that covers both clinical and managerial domains. Secondly, from a research evidence viewpoint, none of the approaches stands out as being more successful in healthcare than any of the others. Having an improvement method or model can make a significant difference to achieving outcomes but it does not seem to matter which approach it is. The authors conclude that the process of improvement is more important than the specific approach or method. When quality improvement efforts fail to deliver, it is rarely an "approach" problem or a "tool" problem. Rather, it is a "human dynamics" or "leadership" problem. Thirdly, for healthcare leaders, seriously adopting and committing to the method for as long as it takes to deliver the results for patients is as important as selecting the specific method of improvement.

Fourthly, there are many paths (and many method options) to successful, sustained quality improvement. The most important factor is the leadership ability to address many simultaneous challenges and to adapt solutions and strategies to the organisation's own context.

I welcome this report as an important contribution to the body of evidence on quality in healthcare at a time when quality improvement is rightfully gaining a high strategic priority in the NHS. And I am delighted that, after four years, a report that has so much to teach those of us who want to provide safe, effective care and a great patient experience has finally seen the light of day!

Helen Bevan
Chief of Service Transformation
NHS Institute for Innovation and Improvement

Table Of Contents

Table Of Contents

Table Of Contents

Table Of Contents

Tables

Figures

Glossary

5S	Sort, simplify/straighten/set in order, shine/scrub, standardise/stabilise, sustain/self discipline
A&E	Accident and Emergency
BB	Black Belt
BPR	Business Process Reengineering
CLAB	Central line associated bloodstream (infection)
CQI	Continuous Quality Improvement
DBR	Drum – Buffer - Rope
DFSS	Design for Six Sigma
DMADV	Define – Measure – Analyse – Design – Verify (a Six Sigma DFSS roadmap)
DMAIC	Define – Measure – Analyse – Improve – Control (the main Six Sigma roadmap)
DoH	Department of Health (UK)
DPMO	Defects Per Million Opportunities
EBD	Experience Based Design
EFQM	European Foundation for Quality Management
GB	Green Belt
GE	General Electric company
IHI	Institute for Healthcare Improvement
JIT	Just in time (supply of materials etc.)
MA	NHS Modernisation Agency (2001-2005)
MBB	Master Black Belt
MCN	Managed Clinical Networks
NHS	National Health Service
NDP	National Demonstration Project
NHS Institute	NHS Institute for Innovation and Improvement
OPT	Optimised Production Technology
PCT	Primary Care Trust
PDCA	Plan - Do - Check - Act cycle
PDSA	Plan - Do - Study - Act
RCT	Randomised Controlled Trial
RIE	Rapid Improvement Event
SD	Standard Deviation
SPC	Statistical Process Control
ToC	Theory of Constraints
TPS	Toyota Production System
TPs	Thinking Processes
TQI	Total Quality Improvement
TQM	Total Quality Management
VOC	Voice of the Customer
VUT	A formula for calculating waiting time in a queue based on system Variability, Utilisation and (processing) Time

Executive Summary

This report, written in conjunction with the Manchester Business School, focuses on quality improvement in healthcare, and summarises the evidence about how it has been implemented and the results of this process.

It has a focus on the role of various industrial quality improvement approaches in this process: the Plan-Do-Study-Act (PDSA) cycle, Statistical Process Control, Six Sigma, Lean, Theory of Constraints and Mass Customisation. It also outlines the development of quality from a clinical perspective and the way in which industrial approaches are now being applied in healthcare.

The report draws on academic literature as well as other sources, including accounts published on the web, but recognises the methodological limitations of accounts of success in quality improvement without any comparative data being made available.

The purpose of this report is:

- to provide a guide to the main approaches being used, in terms of their context as well as their impact. This shows the emphasis and focus of these approaches, so that guidance on the situations where they might be most effective can be developed

- to enable links to be made between aspects of quality improvement which are often regarded as separate; specifically improvement from clinical and organisational perspectives.

Where did the information come from?

The information was obtained from searches of academic databases, grey literature sources as well as the prior knowledge of the authors and staff from the NHS Institute for Innovation and Improvement (NHS Institute).

How robust is the information?

Relatively few papers which provided analytical reviews of the application of improvement approaches were found; most appeared to be descriptive case studies based on a single site. These were relatively small scale before and after studies, making it difficult to determine whether any reported changes are directly attributable to the quality improvement intervention or not.

The papers found used a wide range of methods to gather the data reported. A debate about the relevance (or otherwise) of randomised controlled trial methods to investigate the effectiveness of quality improvement approaches was also identified. Some authors argued that quality improvement is a complex social intervention, for which methods designed to 'control out' the influence of context on the implementation of the intervention are not relevant.

Executive Summary

This report concludes that a number of methods are needed and that no single one will be sufficient to assess the full impact of quality improvement. More focus on how a particular approach can be used is needed, since research to date shows that most approaches work sometimes, although there is little evidence about which contextual factors influence this.

Clinical quality improvement

The history of clinical quality improvement goes back to conceptualisations of clinical work as craft with individuals responsible for the quality of the outcome, and as early as 1916 Codman focused on the end results system of auditing clinical care. Other individuals with a significant influence on clinical quality improvement include Donabedian, who outlined a definition of quality which focused on structure, process and outcome, and Berwick, who spearheaded the application of industrial approaches within a clinical environment.

Influences on the development of clinical quality improvement include clinical audit, clinical guidelines, care pathways and clinical governance, with recent attempts to integrate these more closely with organisational issues.

What is quality?

Quality can be defined in a variety of ways, and increasingly the terms quality and safety are being used interchangeably. This report shows that safety may be regarded as one element of quality, with the most widely used definition probably being that of quality as healthcare that is safe, effective, patient-centred, timely, efficient and equitable.

Assessing quality as an element of performance can be complex; a 'balancing act' between organisational and clinical aspects, as well as process and outcomes. This is a challenge for healthcare systems in many contexts.

Industrial approaches to quality improvement

These developed in manufacturing industry, in practice after the Second World War, but being based on earlier statistical approaches developed in the 1920s. Key figures (gurus) who influenced this process include Deming, Juran, Crosby and Feigenbaum, and their approaches share a common focus on the role of customers and management as well as teamwork, systematic approach to work and the use of appropriate improvement tools, whilst differing in their emphasis on these factors.

Executive Summary

Many elements of these approaches were incorporated into Total Quality Management (TQM) in the 1980s which attempted to apply quality improvement at the organisational level, although as an approach it has not been shown to be very successful. This is not dissimilar to other organisation-wide approaches to change and improvement, including Business Process Re-engineering (BPR). Frameworks for assessing organisational quality were also developed, linked to 'awards' in Japan, the USA and Europe.

At the same time, there was an increasing focus on quality improvement in service organisations, with the development of service quality as a field of study. This necessitated more focus on marketing and relationship with customers, as well as the role of staff in quality improvement.

Quality improvement approaches

Plan-Do-Study-Act (PDSA) cycle

- *Outline of the approach*: The plan-do-study-act (PDSA) model was developed by Deming (Deming 1986) – and termed by him the Shewhart cycle (Dale 2003). Deming's initial terminology was plan-do-check-act (PDCA), but he later changed this to PDSA to better reflect his thinking. PDSA is the term generally used in healthcare and which will therefore be used here. PDSA cycles are small tests of change, used as part of a continuous improvement approach. A change practitioner will plan a test of change, carry out the change (do), study the results and act on them in the next cylce of change.

- *How the approach fits with others*: there are few reports of the approach being used with others, although tools from a variety of approaches can be used at any stage of the PDSA cycle and PDSA is sometimes suggested in the 'improve' phase of Six Sigma and as part of Rapid Improvement Events in Lean.

- *Where the approach has been used in healthcare*: it has been widely used, particularly as the main framework for the collaborative approach – the 'breakthrough' approach to improvement. The impact appears to depend on the focus of the collaborative, the participants and their host organisation and the style and method of implementing the collaborative.

- *Outcomes that have been reported*: the approach has been relatively well studied in terms of its application in healthcare (compared with the other approaches considered in this report) although there is little evidence (to date) to suggest it is more cost-effective that any other approach. The longer term impact in terms of sustainability and spread of the approach has not yet been evaluated.

Executive Summary

Statistical Process Control (SPC)

- *Outline of the approach*: The roots of this approach can be traced to work by Shewhart in the 1920s which identified the difference between 'natural' variation in measures of a process – termed 'common cause' - and that which could be controlled – 'special' or 'assignable' cause variation. Processes that exhibited only common cause variation were said to be in statistical control. It is argued that the use of this approach for quality improvement gave it a scientific and statistical focus.

- *How the approach fits with others*: it was widely promoted as a key tool in the TQM approach, is also used in Six Sigma and sometimes with Theory of Constraints and the PDSA cycle. Some argue that its growth would have been more rapid if it did not challenge the focus on short-term cost reduction, which is often one element in quality improvement. It provides guidance for action in a way which more conventional statistical analyses do not.

- *Where the approach has been used in healthcare*: recognition of the importance of variation in healthcare has led to an interest in SPC, with a wide variety of applications reported. Systematic review of SPC application in patient monitoring found it to be a simple, low-cost and effective approach although there is always debate about its applicability. It is used both to report performance data at board level and to provide guidance for healthcare practitioners on treatment effectiveness.

- *Outcomes that have been reported*: systematic review showed that SPC could be used to improve communication between clinicians, managers and patients by providing a shared language, to describe and quantify variation, to identify areas for potential improvement and to assess the impact of change interventions. Its application may be limited by the extent to which the objective of improvement is the reduction of variation, the complexity and appropriateness of data sets representing aggregations of different types of patients or management units and the implications on the underlying statistics of having very small or very large data sets.

Six Sigma

- *Outline of the approach*: Six Sigma is an improvement or (re)design approach developed initially by Motorola in the 1980s, initially in manufacturing, although it is now becoming popular in the service sector especially with US-owned firms. It has its roots in the work of Shewhart and Deming, but there is no universally accepted definition. However, most authors agree that it may be regarded as a method for process improvement and product development that utilises a systematic approach, relying on statistical methods to improve defect rates (as defined by the customer). It consists of:

  o an underlying philosophy of identifying customer needs and then establishing the root causes of variation in meeting these needs

  o elements that support this, including a certification structure for various levels of competence in applying the approach (black and green 'belts') and a structured

Executive Summary

> way of deploying the approach and coaching of projects throughout the organisation, supported by training
>
> o structured methodologies (including define, measure, analyse, improve and control (DMAIC)) are used
>
> o these are supported by a variety of tools for improvement, many of which are common to other quality improvement approaches

- *How the approach fits with others*: many organisations appear to have re-labelled TQM as Six Sigma, and a recent development is the use of Lean Six Sigma (see following section)

- *Where the approach has been used in healthcare*: there are numerous reports of the application of Six Sigma but few that take a systematic approach to assessing its effectiveness. The approach is heavily promoted in the US, in line with its current popularity in all types of organisations

- *Outcomes that have been reported:* the evidence is descriptive, with no fundamental critique or examination of its effectiveness, or independent evaluation. This may be due to its relatively recent popularity, with a number of academics acknowledging that the academic perspective is currently lagging the practice.

Lean

- *Outline of the approach*: The term Lean has been developed in the context of manufacturing from the way in which Toyota, and other Japanese motor manufacturers, organise their production processes. The approach can be described as either:

  o the five principles of Lean: identify customer value, manage the value stream, 'flow' production, pull work through the process and pursue perfection through reducing all forms of waste in the system, or

  o the 'Toyota Production System' (TPS) as summarised in the 'Toyota Way: problem-solving, people and partners, process and philosophy'.

  A variety of tools can be used to support the Lean approach, many of which are common to other approaches, and there is no definitive list. Commonly used ones include value stream mapping, rapid improvement events and 5S (sort, simplify/straighten/set in order, shine/scrub, standardise/stabilise, sustain/self discipline).

- *How the approach fits with others*: many authors believe that Lean can be integrated with other approaches. The most common integration appears to be with Six Sigma, to form Lean Six Sigma, although some argue that this has been because of diminishing returns from the use of either approach on its own. Most of these attempts bring Lean tools and approaches into the overall Six Sigma framework (most often the DMAIC methodology). Some authors describe the different focus of Lean (reducing waste) and Six Sigma (identifying cause and effect) and arguing that organisations need both.

- *Where the approach has been used in healthcare*: there is an increasing emphasis on Lean approaches in healthcare, with some authors arguing that its features make it especially

Executive Summary

applicable, as well as a developing community of those using the approach. In particular, the complexity of healthcare processes, the difficulty in seeing where there are problems and the inappropriate measures of performance are highlighted. Some authors argue that Lean needs to be adapted to be successfully applied to services. They believe that Lean has an inappropriate focus on standardisation of work and the definition of value from a customer perspective, when customers may be multiple and their needs hard to identity. There is some empirical evidence to support the need for Lean to be adapted if it is to be successfully implemented in public sector organisations. There is a wide range of 'how to' guides available for implementing Lean in healthcare, but it is difficult to identify an evidence base for the guidance.

- *Outcomes that have been reported*: evidence from manufacturing shows that Lean is beneficial, with most studies having focused on one aspect of Lean and focused on quantitative and comparative research. Within healthcare there are numerous reports of the application of Lean but, as with Six Sigma, these are not comparative, independent or critical.

Theory of Constraints

- *Outline of the approach*: Theory of Constraints (ToC) developed from the Optimised Production Technology (OPT) system first proposed by Goldratt in the early 1980s. The basic concepts of ToC are that every system has at least one constraint - anything that limits the system from achieving higher performance in terms of its goal, and the existence of constraints represents opportunities for improvement. The approach consists of three elements:

  o the pre-requisites (establishing the goal of the system and what performance measurement system will support its achievement)

  o the thinking processes: a set of logic tools to establish and communicate what to change, what to change to, and how to bring about the change

  o the five focusing steps: identify the system's constraints, decide how to exploit them, subordinate everything else to that, elevate the system's constraints, if a constraint is broken, repeat the process.

  The drum-buffer-rope method for managing constraints is key: the rate of work of the constraint sets the pace for the whole process.

- *How the approach fits with others*: the approach tends to be exclusive, though it has been used with SPC in some situations.

- *Where the approach has been used in healthcare*: there are relatively few accounts of its application in healthcare that use empirical data although there is some theoretical work, and where accounts are available they are anecdotal and fragmented. Within the NHS there is some evidence of the thinking processes being used and more of the five focusing steps; buffer management is becoming quite common, supported by software, being used to improve achievement of A&E target times and expected inpatient target discharge dates.

Executive Summary

- *Outcomes that have been reported:* there are numerous accounts of the application of ToC in industry in general, but little in healthcare and that data which is available lacks rigour in the way it has been gathered.

Mass Customisation

- *Outline of the approach*: The approach focuses on the ability to produce products or services in high volume, yet vary their specification to the needs of individual customers or type of customer and is closely linked to variation. It attempts to address the conflict between high volume, 'mass production' of services which is often linked to lower unit cost and lower volume higher variety services, with higher associated costs but increased customer satisfaction and fit of service with customer needs.

- *How the approach fits with others*: while not strictly an approach to quality improvement, its focus on system and process design means it is closely linked with improvement since system and process design has been shown to have a major impact on quality.

- *Where the approach has been used in healthcare*: despite a lot of evidence for its use in manufacturing, there is little to show how it has been applied in healthcare, despite increasing theoretical emphasis on its potential to support healthcare improvement.

- *Outcomes that have been reported*: there are to date no independently reported results of the application of mass customisation in healthcare.

Underlying concepts

The approaches to quality improvement detailed in this report are all based on a series of underlying concepts, with different emphasis on each one depending on the approach concerned. The report outlines these concepts and demonstrates how they support the various approaches to quality improvement, as well as the implications for using the approaches in practice. These concepts might be described as those underlying operations management, a well-established academic discipline, although the concepts are described in different ways by different authors.

Every organisation has a function that can be described as 'operations'. Operations management focuses on examining the processes used to produce goods and services. Effective operations management has the potential to keep costs down, improve revenue, appropriately allocate resources and develop future competitive advantage, although research in healthcare rarely take an operations management perspective.

Systems and processes

The systems view is fundamental both to operations management and to much of the thinking around improvement, particularly to Deming's insights. This may make operations management approaches applicable in healthcare, which also focuses on the whole system.

Executive Summary

- *Systems thinking in healthcare* is especially apparent when network forms of organisation of healthcare services are considered. There is an increasing body of evidence supporting the effectiveness of this form of organisation, and the benefits in terms of sharing knowledge which result.

- *The process view* is essentially systems thinking at a more detailed level, down to the work of individuals within systems viewed as comprising series of processes. Healthcare often appears to experience conflict between clinical and managerial processes, with improvement approaches applied to one or the other, rather than considering how they might be integrated.

- *Process design in healthcare* is underpinned by a series of principles for any process design, which include consideration of explicit and implicit benefits from the process for the customer (e.g. the patient) as well as design of the way in which the service is delivered and the goods required to support this activity. There is a wide range of process redesign activity within healthcare, sometimes labelled as one of the quality improvement approaches (particularly Lean).

- *Managing flow* is one element of process management and is the emphasis for the Lean approach to improvement, with ToC also considering this. It is argued that consideration of flow will lead to systems thinking since flow through one element of the healthcare system cannot be considered in isolation.

- *Variation* underpins many of the quality improvement approaches, specifically SPC and Six Sigma. Lean and ToC will have an impact on variation although it is not the main focus of the approaches, whilst it is an explicit input to the mass customisation process. The extent to which variation is inherent in healthcare processes, and thus can be reduced (or not) is a matter of debate.

The role of the customer

The customer has an important role in defining quality in most of the approaches in this report – particularly Lean and Six Sigma. In healthcare it is not necessarily the patient who is the customer; other stakeholders may include carers, society, taxpayers (where the system is publicly funded) and the processes by which decisions are made (which may dictate certain steps in a process which would otherwise be regarded as unnecessary).

Balancing supply and demand

Generally there is little evidence that well-established approaches for managing this inevitable tension in other industries are being applied in healthcare, in anything other than a piecemeal way.

- *Capacity management*: whilst a necessary part of any service provision, there is little evidence of its explicit consideration within healthcare. Bed management is one activity which attempts to manage capacity. Strategies for managing capacity include:

Executive Summary

- o level capacity with resultant queues at times of excess demand
- o chase demand by adjusting capacity to meet demand, which often has an impact on the quality of service
- o 'Coping', which is often an unintentional strategy and may again lead to decline in quality of service.

- *Demand management*: there is some evidence of this in healthcare but only to a limited extent. Of more importance perhaps is the extent of 'failure demand' – when services are provided again because the customer was not satisfied the first time or because an alternative service is not available when required.

- *Inventory management*: the major example of this within healthcare is queues (waiting lists) for services.

Translating improvement approaches to the healthcare context

Healthcare may be regarded as different from other sectors because it is a professional service, with a complex structure and a history of being difficult and complex to change, for a variety of reasons. The NHS is particularly complex due to the autonomy of its many stakeholder groups and the lack of connection between much resource decision making and financial consequences.

The implications of translating these approaches are important when the impact on people is considered. Organisational culture, which stems from the beliefs of those who comprise the organisation, as well as leadership are shown to be influential. Assumptions that the workforce at large are motivated to change for the sake of improved quality of care are challenged by some authors, while others highlight the need for long-term stability of employment if quality improvement is to be successful.

Does quality improvement work?

Whilst the evidence for the effectiveness of particular approaches to quality improvement has already been considered, and shown to be lacking in many cases, there are some wider studies which consider the impact of quality improvement as a generic organisational change, rather than any single labelled approach. Issues of methodology – and in particular the lack of comparative studies – are raised, as it is the issue of definition of quality improvement.

While a number of lists of success factors have been produced, some of which are based on extensive empirical evidence, it is clear that the main issue is the way in which the improvement is implemented, rather than the nature of the improvement itself.

1. INTRODUCTION

This report focuses on quality improvement in healthcare, and summarises the evidence about how it has been implemented and the results of this process.

It has a focus on the role of various industrial quality improvement approaches in this process: the Plan-Do-Study-Act (PDSA) cycle, Statistical Process Control, Six Sigma, Lean and Theory of Constraints. It also outlines the development of quality from a clinical perspective and the way in which industrial approaches are now being applied in healthcare.

The report draws on academic literature as well as other sources, including accounts published on the Web, but recognises the methodological limitations of accounts of success in quality improvement without any comparative data being made available.

The purpose of this report is:

- to provide a guide to the main approaches being used, in terms of their context as well as their impact
- to highlight the different focus for improvement that underpins these approaches, so that guidance on the situations where they might be most effective can be developed
- to enable links to be made between aspects of quality improvement which are often regarded as separate; specifically improvement from clinical and organisational perspectives

This review is limited in that it is not a full systematic review, although the intention was to cover all the main areas of literature. We have attempted to include all key sources, but apologise if something has been missed. We hope that this review can act as a starting point for some integration of the diverse literature and evidence on quality improvement which can contribute to the improvement of healthcare quality in practice through clearer understanding.

1.1 Who should read the report?

This report will be helpful for:

- Clinicians
- Chief Executives of PCTs, NHS Trusts, SHAs and other NHS organisations
- Chairs of PCTs, PECs and NHS Trust Boards
- Directors: including those with responsibility for clinical care, nursing, operations, strategy, performance, improvement and human resources
- NHS improvement leaders
- Those in pre-registration or vocational training who are studying healthcare quality and improvement

1.2 Which parts of the report are most relevant?

Whilst the whole of the report contains information that will be helpful for those reading it, in order to guide readers from different backgrounds the following is suggested:

If you:
- have little time ... read the Executive Summary and the Conclusions (section 8)
- have some time but do not want all the detail ... follow the Executive Summary by reading the sections on the development of quality and improvement in healthcare and industry (sections 3 and 4), the description of the concepts underlying the various approaches (section 6) and the section on translating improvement approaches to healthcare (section 7). This misses out all the detail on the various approaches
- are interested in how the evidence in this report was gathered ... read section 2
- want to know what evidence was used ... look at the list of references at the end of the body of the report
- want to know more about the context and development of quality in healthcare ... read section 3
- want to understand the development of industrial methods for quality improvement ... read section 4
- want to know about a particular approach to improvement: Plan-Do-Study-Act (PDSA) cycle Statistical Process Control (SPC), Six Sigma, Lean, Theory of Constraints, Mass Customisation ... read the relevant part of section 5
- want to know what these approaches have in common, and the principles which they emphasise ... read section 6
- want to know where improvement approaches have been applied in healthcare and the outcomes that have been reported ... read the third and fourth part of the sub-section about each approach in section 5
- want to know more about translating industrial improvement approaches to healthcare ... read section 7

1.3 Presentation style

- There are a large number of references to published work in the report; these are shown in the text by the author(s) and the year of publication and then listed in alphabetical order by author from page 85
- Throughout the text boxes are used to highlight key points and to provide explanation of terminology used
- A glossary of key terms and abbreviations can be found on page 8.

Quality Improvement: Theory and Practice in Healthcare

2. INFORMATION SOURCES AND METHODOLOGY

2.1 Where did the information come from?

This report is based on reviews of available evidence about the effectiveness of various quality improvement approaches, and their application in healthcare. The methods used to gather this information are described in subsequent sections. However, the way in which the evidence has been synthesised and presented is the responsibility of the authors of the report, and does not in any way represent UK National Health Service (NHS) policy.

2.1.1 Database searches

This review did not employ formal systematic review methods, however a number of semi-systematic searches on the key approaches described were carried out. In general these yielded very few papers which provided analytical reviews of the application of improvement approaches; most appeared to be descriptive case studies based on a single site. These were relatively small scale, before and after studies, making it difficult to determine whether any reported changes are directly attributable to the quality improvement intervention or not.

It was also notable that many projects applied quality improvement approaches to support processes within the healthcare sector (e.g. pathology) or to those patient care processes which have clear parallels with industrial processes (e.g. radiography) rather than processes directly providing patient care.

2.1.2 Grey literature

Grey literature can be defined as *"Information produced on all levels of government, academics, business and industry in electronic and print formats not controlled by commercial publishing i.e. where publishing is not the primary activity of the producing body."*[1]. Given the diversity of grey (i.e. information not formally published) literature, we did not make any attempt to search this type of literature in a systematic sense, but followed up sources recommended or known to us as well as using links from the websites of the NHS Institute for Innovation and Improvement (NHS Institute) and the Institute for Healthcare Improvement (IHI).

We received anecdotal information about the application of various approaches across the world, but have concentrated here on information 'published' in some form and publicly available through the web or from academic journals. It should be noted that we have formed the impression that there is an increasing amount of information about improvement being published and we have done our best to ensure that the information here is up to date.

2.   http://www.greynet.org/

2.1.3 Prior knowledge

Due to work by various members of the team in previous research and consultancy, they were able to bring information and knowledge to the research. A brief résumé of the research team and their background is given in Appendix 1. We have also utilised the experience of staff from the NHS Institute to supplement literature found through formal searching.

2.2 Methodology: How robust is this information?

There are several issues to consider when information about quality improvement is presented: not only concerning the appropriateness of the methods by which this information has been gathered, but also the nature of the information itself and its scope and completeness, and whether calls for a new field of research should be heeded.

2.2.1 The relevance of controlled trials

There are few large-scale, rigorously conducted trials (from a scientific perspective) that provide conclusive evidence to support the assertion that implementing quality improvement programmes and methods leads to improved processes and outcomes of care (Perneger 2006). Typically, randomised controlled trials (RCTs) are designed to evaluate the impact of a single, discrete intervention (for example, the introduction of a new surgical technique for joint replacement), where the aim is to establish causality (i.e. new techniques leads to improved patient outcomes). In the design and conduct of the study, the focus is on controlling for as many extraneous variables as possible to limit any unintended bias. An RCT, by definition, tends to 'control out' the context-dependent variables that are argued by some to determine the success or failure of the intervention (Pawson, Greenhalgh, Harvey et al. 2005).

A review of quality improvement research (Grol, Baker & Moss 2004) summarises the methods used to date as:

- audits of care
- determinants of variations in care provision
- studies of the effectiveness of change strategies (mostly trials)

In addition, there is a prevalence of case reports and before-and-after papers, which are able to disseminate results quickly, although *"weak designs ... do not allow internally valid conclusions and the consequence is that the science of quality improvement will proceed ineffectively in healthcare"* (Speroff & O'Connor 2004).

Recent work has argued that urgency and robust evidence are not alternative choices: *"it is both possible and wise to remain alert and vigilant for problems while testing promising changes very rapidly and with a sense of urgency"* (Berwick 2008, p.1183)

Trials may not be an appropriate method for researching quality improvement because ...

... they do not promote learning: *"The RCT is a powerful, perhaps unequalled, research design to explore the efficacy of conceptually neat components of clinical practice – tests, drugs, procedures. For other crucially important learning purposes, however, it serves less well"* (Berwick 2008, p.1182). *"'Where is the randomized trial?' is, for many purposes, the right question, but for many others it is the wrong question, a myopic one. A better one is broader: 'What is everyone learning?'"* (Berwick 2008, p.1184).

... they impede progress: emphasis on experimental methods *"can seriously hamper those both researching and implementing quality improvement in healthcare"* (Walshe 2007, p.57).

... it is not feasible or ethical to apply them (Speroff & O'Connor 2004).

... they are not sensitive to the things that influence the success of change: the *"array of influences: leadership, changing environments, details of implementation, organizational history, and much more"* that influence the 'success' of change and describe the RCT as an *"impoverished way to learn"* (Berwick 2008, p.1183).

2.2.2   Quality improvement is a complex social intervention

Those questioning the use of experimental methods also argue that they are not appropriate in *"investigating and understanding complex social interventions"* (Walshe 2007, p.57). Like many other organisational level change management programmes, quality improvement can be described as a complex intervention that typically involves a number of inter-related components e.g. training in specific improvement methods and approaches, the creation of improvement teams, data feedback, tailored facilitation and support (Lilford 2003). Complex interventions are characteristically active, non-linear, embedded in social systems, and prone to modification and change (Pawson et al. 2005), and these factors are important to take into account when designing evaluations.

Some claim that quality improvement methods *"were never intended to stand up to the rigour demanded in a full-scale medical research study"* (Plsek 1999).

There is an increasing emphasis on context as a key influence on implementation (Walshe 2007) with consideration of content (the nature of the intervention itself) as well as application (the process through which the intervention is delivered) and the outcomes (results) of the intervention.

In order to address the more complex nature of the intervention, staged approaches such as the Medical Research Council's framework for evaluating complex interventions have been developed (Campbell, Fitzpatrick, Haines et al. 2000). This is a phased approach using different research methods in each phase; following a theoretical phase, the components of the intervention are defined, an exploratory trial carried out followed by an RCT and then long term implementation. However, many authors are now arguing for more than one method to be used.

2.2.3 Is more than one methodology needed?

Given the broad scope and focus of quality improvement and the fact that it draws on knowledge and learning from a range of disciplines both within healthcare and outside, it seems likely that a range of research approaches and methodologies may be considered appropriate to evaluate its implementation (Grol, Berwick & Wensing 2008). The need to conduct the research both rigorously and ethically remains paramount, but the use of other methods does not imply that rigour must be sacrificed (Berwick 2008).

The key issues concerning methodology focus on the question which research is trying to address, and it is argued for quality improvement that:

> *"The aim is not to find out 'whether it works', as the answer to that question is almost always 'yes, sometimes'. The purpose is to establish when, how and why the intervention works, to unpick the complex relationship between context, content, application and outcomes"* (Walshe 2007, p.58).

This view is supported by others who emphasise that "the research should focus on understanding why the provision and outcomes of care vary as well as on interventions to change provision" (Grol et al. 2008, p.74).

It is also important to note that simply utilising the most appropriate methodology does not guarantee 'good' research and certainly the pragmatic approach to quality improvement places more emphasis on the outcomes of the research than the methodology used. Given the paucity of literature in the field it was decided that studies using a variety of research methodologies would be included as limiting the criteria of inclusion would have left even fewer studies available. No attempt has been made here to judge research quality.

2.3   Is this a new field of research?

The call for quality improvement (and increasingly patient safety) to develop as an *"important new field for health services research"* (Grol et al. 2004) is growing (Stevens 2005) – although, as highlighted by the preceding discussion, it is debatable whether there can ever be an *"optimal methodology"* (Grol et al. 2004) for this, given the need for different disciplines to collaborate.

The traditional development of an academic field can take many years, although some argue that in the case of healthcare quality improvement, the *"social imperative to make health care better and safer"* means that this is happening more quickly in this area (Stevens 2005).

Recent commentaries on the state of quality improvement research have concluded that perhaps the key issue is that research in this area is not yet fully developed, and may be due to lack of clarity about the research agenda, as well as research capacity and policy emphasis (Grol et al. 2008).

There has been some discussion about the concept of 'improvement science' as a discipline. This term was described as *"knowledge of general truths or the operation of general laws especially that obtained and tested through the scientific method* (Langley, Nolan, Nolan et al. 1996) and it is recognised that in order to improve, knowledge about the problem at hand must be obtained. It is claimed that *"Improvement science is now a central component of healthcare"* (Stevens 2007, p.242).

Searches on academic databases using this term yielded very little apart from:

- the description of the Model for Improvement (Langley et al. 1996)
- a framework for improvement science (Clarke, Reed, Wainwright et al. 2004) with five primary categories:
    - o user needs focused
    - o change methods and strategies – includes learning organisation concepts
    - o knowledge management
    - o professional subject knowledge and development
    - o working in context

    The paper distinguishes between 'modernist' approaches to improvement (technical rationality) which are considered to be relatively mechanistic, and this discipline which emphasises plural voices, dynamics of politics and unequal distribution of power amongst stakeholders, to be more post-modern. Change is also viewed as context specific, with diffusion of innovation principles being universal but practices local
- a paper using the principles of improvement science to improve access to services for children with autism (Manning-Courtney 2007)

It is the view of the authors that there is little justification for the development of a new discipline. The challenges are to integrate the disciplines that already exist, and to reconcile the current conflicts over methodology and epistemology so that healthcare can continue to improve in a way that learns from all perspectives rather than the *"unhappy tension"* (Berwick 2008, p.1182) that currently exists.

QUESTIONS TO THINK ABOUT:

What do you regard as an appropriate methodology to use when finding out how effective quality improvement is?
How much do you take context into account when evaluating whether a particular approach to improvement works?

3. QUALITY IN HEALTHCARE

Two main strands of activity in healthcare quality improvement are evident in the literature, namely those focusing on clinically-led improvement and those concerned with quality from a management perspective. Historically, these have often been treated as discrete, parallel activities within an organisation, with the resulting risk of misaligned objectives, duplication of effort and a lack of focus on the improving both clinical evidence and the process of care (Berwick 2008).

The challenge for healthcare organisations is to improve both clinical and managerial quality, whilst also recognising their interaction. To do this, it is important to understand the roots of both clinical and industrial improvement so that common themes and interactions can be identified.

3.1   The history of clinical quality improvement

From a clinical perspective, the development of quality has been heavily influenced by the medical profession, with its strong roots in a craft-based approach to work, where quality is seen to be almost solely dependent on the skill of the craftspeople. This craft-based approach to professional practice vests the control of quality with individual clinicians, largely at an implicit level, within the overall scope of their professional practice. Consequently, the competence of individual practitioners is a major contributor to the delivery of high quality care; something that has traditionally been regulated through controlling entry into the profession and upholding standards of professional education.

The influence of the craft-based model is apparent in some of the early approaches to quality evaluation in medical practice:

- in outcome-related morbidity and mortality studies, clinical case conferences and the early introduction of medical audit, the emphasis was on closed discussions about quality and standards, typically through applying peer review methods (Harvey 1996)

- as quality became a more prominent feature in healthcare policy, so too more formal requirements for doctors to engage in quality and audit emerged, for example through the mandatory introduction of medical audit in the UK in the late 1980s (Department of Health 1989). For some doctors, these changes were seen as a threat to the traditional craft-based organisation of medical work, resulting in resistance to medical audit and distinctions being drawn between audit as an internal, peer review activity and audit as an external, regulatory mechanism (Shaw 1980).

Throughout these developments, a number of prominent clinicians have challenged traditional ways of thinking and pioneered developments in medical quality evaluation and improvement. An excellent review (Kenney 2008) highlights the role of a number of key individuals:

3.1.1 Codman

As early as 1916, Ernest Codman, a US surgeon, used and published the 'ends results' system of auditing surgical care (Codman 1916). He is acknowledged by many as the founder of outcomes-based patient care. He believed that such information should be made public so that it could guide patient choice of hospital and physician.

3.1.2 Donabedian

In the 1960s and 70s, Avedis Donabedian went further, presenting quality as a multidimensional concept, influenced not just by the technical quality of care, but also by features of the interpersonal relationship between doctor and patient and by the physical amenities of care (Donabedian 1966). Donabedian also promoted an early systems-based approach to thinking about medical quality, with his well-known structure-process-outcome model (see section 3.3.2).

3.1.3 Berwick

Don Berwick has been interested in quality improvement throughout his career as a doctor, but he spent time in the 1980s studying and working on the application of industrial models of quality improvement in healthcare, including that of the quality gurus (see section 4.2). He established the National Demonstration Project on Quality Improvement in Health Care (more commonly known as the National Demonstration Project – NDP) in 1987 which led to the development of a group of like-minded people in US healthcare who could see the possibilities of the application of industrial improvement methods in healthcare.

Berwick has since led the way in calling for a move beyond medical audit towards more improvement-based approaches to quality (Berwick, Endhoven & Bunker 1992) largely because of perceived failures to act on the results of audit to achieve meaningful change. He has published numerous articles and papers, and has an international reputation in this area (Kenney 2008). Berwick and colleagues have proposed that the medical profession needs to look beyond its immediate sphere of knowledge and experience in defining and measuring standards and criteria, towards more general theories of organisational change and industry-based approaches to quality improvement (Berwick 2008). As such, the narrow evaluation of practitioner performance needs to be widened to a more patient/client focused view of quality, with clinicians taking on a so-called new set of clinical skills, incorporating team working, process analysis, guideline development and collaborative working with patients, managers and other professional colleagues (Berwick et al. 1992). There was also a recognition that the medical culture, which discouraged the disclosure of errors, "actually worked against quality improvement" (Kenney 2008) and thus the link between quality and safety was made more explicit.

3.1.4   The role of other clinical professions

Other professional groups in healthcare have been less influenced by the craft-based model of practice, largely as a result of their position in the professional hierarchy relative to medicine. The nursing profession, for example, had its own pioneer of quality and standards in the early work of Florence Nightingale. However, early developments in nursing quality evaluation were largely focused on methods of external monitoring through the development and application of quality indicators and measurement instruments (Harvey 1996). Such developments were superseded by more practitioner-based methods that typically involved local teams of practitioners working together to identify and work on topics for improvement. These approaches had more in common with industry-based approaches such as quality circles, but often failed to become integrated within overall organisational systems for quality management (Morrell, Harvey & Kitson 1997).

3.2   Influences on the development of clinical quality improvement

More recently, developments emanating from the evidence-based medicine movement and from public inquiries into major healthcare failures have introduced a number of new concepts to the field of clinical quality, which may have the potential to create better integration with wider organisational quality initiatives.

3.2.1   Clinical guidelines

The evidence-based practice agenda, with its focus on synthesising existing research through systematic review methods, has contributed to the development of clinical guidelines, described as *"systematically developed statements to assist practitioner and patient decisions about appropriate healthcare for specific clinical circumstances"* ((Institute for Medicine 1992) cited in (Duff, Kitson, Seers et al. 1996, p.888)). A key defining attribute of clinical guidelines is that they should be based on available research evidence (Duff et al. 1996). However, despite the extent of investment in guideline development, evidence to date suggests that their impact on actual practice and patient outcomes is variable (Grimshaw, Thomas, Maclennan et al. 2004), highlighting the challenges and complexities involved in translating evidence into practice.

3.2.2   Care pathways

Care pathways are another tool that has been applied in healthcare in an attempt to standardise processes of care delivery. Pathways have been used in different ways, for example as a way of translating national guidelines into local practice or as a way of mapping ideal processes for specific care groups. Typically they are presented as structured, multidisciplinary plans of care designed to support the implementation of clinical guidelines and protocols, providing guidance about each stage of the management of a patient with a particular condition, including details of both process and outcome. They aim to improve continuity and coordination of care and enable more effective resource planning, as well as providing comparative data on many aspects of quality of care. There are claims they reduce variation and improve outcomes (Middleton, Barnett & Reeves 2001).

3.2.3   Clinical governance

Clinical governance, defined as the "action, the system or the manner of governing clinical affairs" (Lugon & Secker-Walker 1999, p.1), developed as an overall strategy within a policy on quality in the NHS (Department of Health 1989). After a high profile failure of care in a hospital providing paediatric cardiac surgery services which highlighted organisational shortcomings (Kennedy 2001), statutory changes were introduced to impose a legal duty of quality on the chief executives and boards of NHS organisations in the UK, for the first time creating a corporate responsibility for the quality of clinical care. At a strategic level, this policy issued a very strong signal that clinical and managerial processes of managing and improving quality within healthcare organisations needed to be coordinated and led from board level.

3.3   Defining and assessing healthcare quality

3.3.1   Defining quality

Developments in healthcare quality have been professionally led and reflect the different traditions and ways of working within the profession. As a consequence, a range of healthcare definitions and dimensions of quality have developed (see Table 1).

Table 1 - Definitions of healthcare quality

(Donabedian 1987)	(Maxwell 1984)	(Langley et al. 1996)	Institute of Medicine (Hurtado, Swift & Corrigan 2001)
• manner in which practitioner manages the personal interaction with the patient • patient's own contribution to care • amenities of the settings where care is provided • facility in access to care • social distribution of access • social distribution of health improvements attributable to care	• access to services • relevance to need • effectiveness • equity • social acceptability, efficiency and economy	• performance • features • time • reliability • durability • uniformity • consistency • serviceability • aesthetics • personal interaction • flexibility • harmlessness • perceived quality • usability	• safety • effectiveness • patient-centredness • timeliness • efficiency • equity

It should be noted that increasingly the terms quality and safety are being used synonymously and reasons for this may include:

- safety is a pre-requisite for quality: *"achieving a high level of safety is an essential first step in improving the quality of care overall"* (Hurtado, Swift & Corrigan 2001)

- there is *"substantial ambiguity in the definition of patient safety ... the boundary between safety and quality of care is indistinct"*. (Cooper, Sorensen, Anderson et al. 2001, p.2)

- there is a tendency to utilise the most fashionable term; *"patient safety has become the issue 'du jour' and so almost everything gets redefined in that"* (Cooper et al. 2001, p.8)

The variety of definitions of quality, and the implications of this, have been described by a number of authors and it is not necessarily the case that some are right and others wrong: *"several formulations are both possible and legitimate, depending on where we are located in the system of care and on what the nature and extent of our responsibilities are"* (Donabedian 1988). A key paper (Blumenthal 1996) highlights the differences between definitions of quality from the physician, patient, system and purchaser perspectives and concludes that the aim of such a debate is *"the development of approaches to its definition, measurement, and management that integrate the perspectives of the many groups that play a part in the health care system"* (Donabedian 1988).

3.3.2 Process and outcome

Outcomes are not necessarily the same as quality. There is some criticism of the use of outcomes as a major focus of quality, because it can lead to unintended consequences:

> *"We conclude that the use of outcome data and throughput to judge quality of care should be diligently avoided. We have shown that when such measures are used to judge quality of care, they often result in several predictable reactions ranging from resistance to gaming. This response was predicted by Deming ... who argued that the key to improvement was knowledge, and such knowledge would emerge from the incorporation of the scientific method into improvement efforts. For performance management to work it must focus on quality directly—that is on clinical and institutional process."* (Lilford, Mohammed, Spiegelhalter et al. 2004, p.1151)

Donabedian proposed the structure-process-outcome model of quality of care and which has been the basis for much work in healthcare quality since its original description in 1980 (Donabedian 1980). This model can also be used to assess performance in a more general sense where it is assumed that good performance = high quality of care. This model can also be compared with the models for assessing service quality in general which distinguish between the process and the outcome (Johnston & Clark 2005).

Structure = the characteristics of the providers of care – the *"tools and resources (human, physical and financial) they have at their disposal ... the physical and organizational settings in which they work"* (Donabedian 1980, p.81). This definition is wider however than the factors of production and includes the organisation of the staff within the healthcare provider organisation. Structure is essentially relatively stable – it functions to produce care and influences the kind of care that is provided. Structure is relevant to quality (and therefore to performance) in that *"it increases or decreases the probability of good performance"* (Donabedian 1980, p.82).

Process = a set of activities that go on between clinical practitioners and patients. However, this process comprises both technical and interpersonal elements:

- technical = appropriate application of professional knowledge and skills to promote healthcare
- interpersonal = relationship between patients and healthcare professionals, as well as the contextual aspects of care, including amenities – with satisfaction being the appropriate "outcome" here (according to Donabedian).

Technical and interpersonal are also linked – e.g. poor consideration of psychosocial issues can affect technical process performance. Also, maximising technical factors can lead to conflict with interpersonal care e.g. teaching hospitals (see Flood 1994 for examples). Patients can be highly satisfied with bad technical care.

Outcome = a change in the patient's current and future health status – including social and psychological function as well as patient attitudes (including satisfaction), *"health-related knowledge and health-related behavioural change"* (Donabedian 1980, p.83). A broad definition of health is implied here in order to include all these factors.

The reason given by Donabedian for this distinction between process and outcome (which he acknowledges is seen by some as pedantic) is that changes in health status *"do not serve as a measure of the quality of care until other sources for such changes have been eliminated, and one is reasonably sure that previous care is responsible for the change, which can then truly be called an 'outcome'"* (Donabedian 1980, p.83).

This approach can be summarised as *"the structural characteristics of the settings in which care takes place have a propensity to influence the process of care … changes in the process of care … will influence the effect of care on health status, broadly defined"* (Donabedian 1980, p.84). However, it should be noted that *"failures of process do not necessarily result in poor outcomes"* (Crombie & Davies 1998, p.31) because the relationship between health system effectiveness and improved health outcomes *"remains unsettled"* (Arah, Klazinga, Delnoij et al. 2003, p.392). Some studies have however shown a positive relationship between system effectiveness and outcomes (Lilford et al. 2004, Marshall, Shekelle, Leatherman et al. 2000).

QUESTIONS TO THINK ABOUT:

Do you have an agreed definition of quality in your organisation?

Have you considered the relationship between process and outcome measures of quality?

3.3.3 Assessing performance

Performance within the context of healthcare refers to clinical performance and health outcomes for individuals and groups of patients, but also to organisational performance and process data.

> *"Performance … can encompass measures of clinical process, health outcomes, safety, access, efficiency, productivity, employee and user satisfaction, and financial balance, to name but a few"* (Davies, Mannion, Jacobs et al. 2007, p.48)

There is likely to be a predominance of hard quantifiable information (Goddard, Mannion & Smith 1999) and aggregated measures (e.g. star ratings) will often be used, despite the evidence that they can be misleading (Jacobs, Goddard & Smith 2007)

> *"Aggregated measures of complex system performance, especially single ratios, can never capture the "reality" of performance"* (Micheli, Mason, Kennerley et al. 2005, p.70).

> *"Any single performance indicator may be a misleading guide to the overall performance of an organisation as it covers only one dimension of that performance, and concentration on one aspect of care may produce perverse incentives to ignore other aspects of performance. If performance indicators are to be used, it is important that they cover the full range of outputs and inputs for the sector in question "*(Giuffrida, Gravelle & Roland 1999, p.97).

There are a variety of perspectives that can be used when assessing healthcare organisational performance, but it can be argued that some factors are actually outside the control of the organisation. External influences include the fact that care can be provided in other organisational settings before or after the event being studied, the patient themselves can influence performance through, for example, compliance with therapy, and there are the inevitable constraints and incentives imposed on the organisation by the environment (e.g. market competition, regulation).

- *"Organizations protest strongly if they think that measures of their patients' outcomes did not sufficiently consider the severity of illness"* (Flood 1994, p.391)
- *"While health outcome should be related to crude rates of adverse events in the population, performance indicators should relate only to those aspects of care that can be altered by the staff whose performance is being measured"* (Giuffrida et al. 1999, p.97)

- This view is supported by empirical evidence: a number of studies have shown that *"a non-trivial proportion of the variation in the indicators used in the performance assessment system was associated with factors that are not under managerial control"*
- A large proportion of variation in organisational performance has also been shown to be unexplained; 70-80% in one study (Jacobs, Martin, Goddard et al. 2006).

3.3.4 Balancing elements of performance

At a strategic level, many organisations use a so-called balanced scorecard approach to performance measurement to ensure that overall performance is judged against a set of key indicators (financial, internal process, customer and learning and growth measures), thus enabling a more complete picture of quality to be obtained. The challenge for organisations is for leaders to enable balance between the elements, and to ensure that performance measurement and assessment supports the strategy of the organisation.

In practice, there is a danger that some sets of performance metrics get prioritised above others, particularly where external inspection and ranking of organisational performance takes place, as is the case, for example, with many national, government-led performance management systems. Within healthcare this issue is exacerbated by other debates about what constitutes performance and quality, depending on whether the clinical or managerial perspective is dominant (see section 2.4.3).

Focusing on one dimension of quality – in this case, reconfiguration and meeting government performance targets – can lead to serious consequences for patients.

Balancing clinical and organisational priorities: A case of focusing on performance targets at the expense of quality of care

In the English National Health Service (NHS), as in many other healthcare systems across the world, explicit performance monitoring and management by central government is now commonplace. NHS organisations are subject to an annual performance rating, determined by a composite measure of a number of key performance indicators, including financial and waiting time targets, alongside broader measures of performance such as staff and patient survey data.

One hospital (trust) providing acute services was subject to a special investigation by the external regulator for healthcare standards in England and Wales (the Healthcare Commission) following two outbreaks of Clostridium difficile infection, each of which resulted in nineteen patient deaths. The investigation report (Healthcare Commission 2006b) highlighted the failure of senior managers to prioritise infection control, as illustrated by their decision not to set up isolation facilities for infected patients, despite the advice of infection control specialists. This decision was attributed to the management's concern at the cost of establishing an isolation ward and the knock-on effect this would have on the achievement of their key performance targets. The investigation team were particularly critical at the time of the second outbreak of infection, that the organisation's leaders failed to learn from the first outbreak and remained focused on other targets at the expense of managing clinical risk. This is reflected in the following remarks made in the official report of the investigation.

"Following the first major outbreak, the trust's leaders chose to implement some changes but none that might compromise their strategic objectives. They failed to bring the second outbreak quickly under control because they were too focused on the reconfiguration of services and the meeting of the Government's targets, and insufficiently focused on the management of clinical risk. It took the involvement of the Department of Health and national publicity to change their perspective ....The failure of the trust to implement the lessons from the first outbreak, combined with a dysfunctional system for governance which did not incorporate the assessment of risk into its decision making, nor make the board aware of the significance of the outbreaks, meant that it took longer than it should to control the second outbreak. There was a serious failing at the highest levels of the trust to give priority to the management of the second major outbreak. The trust followed neither the advice of its own infection control team nor that of the Health Protection Agency. We are clear that this failing is on the part of the trust and its incorrect interpretation of national priorities. It is our conclusion that the approach taken by the trust compromised the control of infection and hence the safety of patients. This was a significant failing, and we would reiterate to NHS boards that the safety of patients is not to be compromised under any circumstances." (Healthcare Commission 2006b, p.9)

Quality Improvement: Theory and Practice in Healthcare

A review of investigations carried out in organisations where there had been significant failures in terms of patient care (Healthcare Commission 2008) showed that underlying themes included:

- Leadership – especially the board which "must also maintain their focus on clinical quality throughout" (Healthcare Commission 2008, p.8)
- Management and targets – which is argued to have always been part of managing healthcare organisations
- Governance and the use of information
- The impact of organisational change, especially mergers.

It is therefore clear that performance is influenced by a number of factors, but that *"it is not acceptable – nor is it necessary – for the safety of patients to be compromised by any other objectives, no matter how compelling these may seem"* (Healthcare Commission 2008, p.9).

QUESTIONS TO THINK ABOUT:

What measures are used to assess performance in terms of quality in your organisation?

What elements of performance need to be balanced when quality is being assessed?

---

4. INDUSTRIAL QUALITY IMPROVEMENT

4.1   Quality improvement in industry

The academic field of study that is quality management/improvement in general (as opposed to clinical quality improvement) developed from the field of production/operations management, which is itself characterised by an empirical focus (Voss 1995). However, the concept of "quality" and its management is much older, with its formalisation sometimes being attributed to the work of Shewhart on SPC in the 1930s (Shewhart 1931).

As the study of quality as a concept and the management of quality within organisations has developed, a number of academic disciplines have made contributions – including services marketing, organisation studies, human resource management and organisational behaviour, especially change management. The term industrial is used here to reflect the fact that these approaches were first developed and applied within the manufacturing industry, as well as to distinguish them from approaches to clinical quality improvement. However they are now being applied in healthcare (Young, Brailsford, Connell et al. 2004) as later sections of this report will demonstrate.

The appeal of the term quality may be that "it can be used to legitimize all sorts of measures and changes in the name of a self-evident good" (Wilkinson & Willmott 1995). However, the diverse meanings of the term make it "an elusive topic of study" (Wilkinson & Willmott 1995).

The historical perspective is important and an understanding of the geography and development of industry after the Second World War are relevant in this context. Alternative views describe the eras of quality management from inspection through quality control and quality assurance to TQM (Garvin 1988), or by a chronology of events from the Hawthorne studies to 1990 (Martinez-Lorente, Dewhurst & Dale 1998). This review will focus on the key figures in the development of quality improvement and the way in which their ideas have been adapted and adopted, with a particular focus on healthcare.

4.2 The quality gurus

There are a variety of individuals who have influenced the development of quality management and they are often referred to as gurus although there is no definitive list of who might qualify for such a term, and there are probably more influential Japanese gurus than those commonly mentioned. There is however no doubt that the gurus would include the following:

4.2.1 Deming

W E Deming was an American who first went to Japan in 1947 to join a statistical mission documenting the "level of devastation from the war" (Davids 1999). His ideas were adopted by the Japanese and the subsequent success of Japanese manufacturing was attributed to the implementation of these ideas, with the Japanese eventually creating a Deming prize for achievement in product quality.

Deming had been influenced by Shewhart and he was aware of the limits of numbers: "knowing that numbers don't give you the answers, only the questions that need to be asked" (Gabor 1990). Deming developed a 14-point approach (Deming 1986) for his management philosophy for improving quality and changing organisational culture which is shown in Table 2.

Table 2 - Deming's 14 points

Create constancy of purpose toward improvement of product and service, with the aim to become competitive and to stay in business, and to provide jobs
Adopt the new philosophy. We are in a new economic age. Western management must awaken to the challenge, must learn their responsibilities, and take on leadership for change
Cease dependence on inspection to achieve quality. Eliminate the need for inspection on a mass basis by building quality into the product in the first place
End the practice of awarding business on the basis of price tag. Instead, minimise total cost. Move toward a single supplier for any one item, on a long-term relationship of loyalty and trust
Improve constantly and forever the system of production and service, to improve quality and productivity, and thus constantly decrease costs
Institute training on the job
Institute leadership. The aim of supervision should be to help people and machines and gadgets to do a better job. Supervision of management is in need of overhaul, as well as supervision of production workers
Drive out fear, so that everyone may work effectively for the company
Break down barriers between departments. People in research, design, sales, and production must work as a team, to foresee problems of production and in use that may be encountered with the product or service
Eliminate slogans, exhortations, and targets for the work force asking for zero defects and new levels of productivity. Such exhortations only create adversarial relationships, as the bulk of the causes of low quality and low productivity belong to the system and thus lie beyond the power of the work force
Eliminate work standards (quotas) on the factory floor. Substitute leadership
Eliminate management by objective. Eliminate management by numbers, numerical goals Substitute leadership
Remove barriers that rob the hourly worker of his right to pride of workmanship. The responsibility of supervisors must be changed from sheer numbers to quality
Remove barriers that rob people in management and in engineering of their right to pride of workmanship. This means, inter alia, abolishment of the annual or merit rating and of management by objective
Institute a vigorous program of education and self-improvement
Put everybody in the company to work to accomplish the transformation. The transformation is everybody's job

He was also responsible for developing the concept of the PDCA (plan-do-check-action) cycle. As his work developed, he identified the seven "deadly diseases" which he used to criticise Western management and organisational practices. His final contribution was to develop the Deming system of profound knowledge, which is still marketed today but appears to have had relatively less impact than his "14 points" which have undoubtedly been influential in challenging leaders to *"transform the organisation around the concept of continuous improvement"* (Vinzant & Vinzant 1999). However it should be noted that he did not ever use the term Total Quality Management (TQM) and made clear his low regard for it (Petersen 1999). It is also argued that his ideas have influenced the development of the field of strategic management both directly and indirectly (Vinzant & Vinzant 1999).

4.2.2   Juran

In the 1950s Joseph Juran, a member of the team implementing statistical process control (SPC) at the Western Electric Hawthorne works in the 1920s, also went to Japan. He had earlier published his book *The Quality Control Handbook* (Juran 1951) and he focused on the managerial aspects of implementing quality. His approach can be summarised as *quality, through a reduction in statistical variation, improves productivity and competitive position..* He promoted a trilogy of quality planning, quality control and quality improvement and maintained that providing customer satisfaction must be the chief operating goal (Nielsen, Merry, Schyve et al. 2004).

4.2.3   Crosby

Philip Crosby was an American management consultant whose philosophy is summarised as *higher quality reduces costs and raises profit,* and who defined quality as 'conformance to requirements'. He too had 14 steps to quality and his ideas were very appealing to both manufacturing and service organisations, but can be viewed as lacking substance. He is best known for the concepts of *do it right first time* and *zero defects* and believed that management had to set the tone for quality within an organisation.

4.2.4   Feigenbaum

Armand Feigenbaum was the General Electric (GE) chief of manufacturing in the 1960s and he defined quality as a way of managing (rather than a series of technical projects) and the responsibility of everyone. His major contribution was the categorisation of quality costs into: appraisal, prevention and failure, and his insistence that management and leadership are essential for quality improvement. He believed that cost reduction was a result of total quality control. He was the first to use the term total in relation to quality management. His work has been described as relevant to healthcare by Don Berwick (Berwick 1989).

4.2.5 Differences and similarities

From these four - and other - gurus it is very difficult to define an over-arching philosophy. There has been considerable debate about the similarities and differences between the various gurus (Dale 2003) - the differences are ascribed to the focus of their approach (Dale 2003). It is argued that the 'golden thread' through all their approaches is adopting quality as a fundamental business strategy permeating the culture of the whole organisation (McBryde 1986). The key points are summarised by (Bendell, Penson & Carr 1995) as:

- management commitment and employee awareness are essential (Deming)
- actions need to be planned and prioritised (Juran)
- teamwork plays a vital part (Ishikawa – who pioneered the quality circle concept)
- tools are needed (e.g. seven quality control tools promoted by Ishikawa)
- management tools/approaches will also be needed (Feigenbaum)
- customer focus (Deming)

Some authors argue that whilst some of the gurus were working in Japan to pursue *"unending improvement and innovation through mobilising the entire workforce in pursuit of these aims"*, the West was focusing on *"conformance to standards, control of processes and command of personnel"* (Wright 1997). It is only from the 1980s onwards that the West has been working to cross this divide.

"Can the gurus' concepts cure healthcare?" (Nielsen et al. 2004)

This paper examined the state of quality in healthcare in the US, then asking four experts to surmise what four quality "gurus" might say. Their conclusions were that:

- Crosby would continue to emphasise the role of leadership in pursuing zero defects

- Deming would continue to emphasise transformation (as he did in the 14th of his 14 points – see Table 2) whilst being disappointed at the reactive behaviour of healthcare organisations and individuals with *"far too little pursuit of constant improvement"* (Nielsen et al. 2004)

- Feigenbaum would focus on clearer identification of the customer and the application of evidence based medicine

- Juran's emphasis would be on building quality into processes from the start (what he termed 'quality planning').

Quality Improvement: Theory and Practice in Healthcare

4.3 Total Quality Management

Other terminology that is also used to describe quality improvement includes Total Quality Management (TQM), Continuous Quality Improvement (CQI) (McLaughlin & Simpson 1999) and Total Quality Improvement (TQI) (Iles & Sutherland 2001). Such terms appear to be interchangeable in usage (although whether their meaning is the same is the subject of some debate (Larson & Muller 2002/3)). The link between quality management and TQM has been the subject of much speculation (Dahlgaard 1999).

It may be that *"[TQM] has become mainly a banner under which a potpourri of essentially unrelated organisational changes are undertaken" (Hackman & Wageman 1995). TQM is considered by some to be particularly attractive in practice because it offers "a unified set of principles which can guide managers through the numerous choices [open to them] or might even make choosing unnecessary"* (Huczynski 1993).

This is not the appropriate place to provide a full review of what TQM is, or how it has been implemented in both the US and the UK. Suffice to say, there is significant disagreement about how it can be defined, what it constitutes and whether it was simply a fad. However, TQM is usually described as a *"management philosophy and business strategy"* (Iles and Sutherland, 2001 p.48) and the common themes may be summarised as (Berwick et al. 1992, Hackman & Wageman 1995):

* organisational success depends on meeting customer needs, including internal customers
* quality is an effect caused by the processes within the organisation which are complex but understandable
* most human beings engaged in work are intrinsically motivated to try hard and do well
* simple statistical methods, linked with careful data collection, can yield powerful insights into the causes of problems within processes

Thus, TQM can be regarded as including many of the approaches/tools described in this review.

4.4   Applying approaches from manufacturing in the service sector

Until the 1980s most of the emphasis on quality improvement, and most of the empirical utilisation of the associated tools, was within manufacturing industry. However, the field of service quality developed with input from marketing academics – led from Scandinavia (Groonroos 1984) and the US (Berry, Zeithaml & Parasuraman 1985). One of the most commonly utilised tools from this period is the SERVQUAL questionnaire (Parasuraman, Zeithaml & Berry 1988). The concept of the 'moment of truth' and an emphasis on service recovery were also prominent. This development was also underpinned by the increasing economic importance of the service sector in the West.

The nature of service organisations as more people-intensive than much of manufacturing led to increasing interest in the role of people in quality improvement and to a tension between 'hard' (systems) approaches and 'soft' (people/culture) issues (Wilkinson 1992). This was also driven by concerns about the promotion of TQM as a universal panacea, regardless of context, and of its disinclination to *"refer to previous management literature – or, indeed, to reference anything outside of the quality management field"* (Wilkinson & Willmott 1995). The gradual emergence of a field comprised largely of prescriptive research was also influential. Change management/ organisational behaviour perspectives became more prominent (Hackman & Wageman 1995) with summaries of such studies being produced (Webb 1995).

4.5   Quality awards and business excellence

Achievements in the area of quality improvement have been increasingly the subject of national awards. The Deming Application Prize (Japan) led to the development of the Malcolm Baldrige National Quality Award (USA) and then in Europe to the European Foundation for Quality Management (EFQM) Award/ Excellence Model (Europe), with its associated national and sector-specific derivatives. Quality was increasingly assessed by organisations themselves as a means of improvement: what is termed self-assessment (European Foundation for Quality Management 1999). These models attempted to integrate the hard and soft factors, and the term quality appeared to be replaced by 'excellence'.

4.6   Business Process Re-engineering

The Business Process Reengineering (BPR) approach to improvement was first described in the early 1990s (Hammer & Champy 1993) to describe the redesign of business processes. It can be summarised as having a series of underpinning concepts (Iles & Sutherland 2001):

- organisations should be organised around key processes rather than specialist functions
- narrow specialists should be replaced by multi-skilled workers, often working in self managed teams
- BPR requires radical rethinking, not incremental improvement
- the direction for this rethinking comes from top management

There is a relatively substantial evidence base about the success (or otherwise) of BPR but it is beset by the same methodological issues as TQM, and as improvement initiatives in general and many initiatives reported have only considered the re-engineering of a single process rather than the whole organisation. Reviews of the key initiatives within the NHS (McNulty & Ferlie 2002) argue there is conflict between this revolutionary approach and the belief that consideration of context is important in securing organisational change (Buchanan 1997). Experience of BPR has shown that a purely top-down imposed approach is unlikely to succeed (Iles & Sutherland 2001).

QUESTIONS TO THINK ABOUT:
Do you think that it is helpful to focus improvement efforts around a particular guru or label? To what extent might the fact that healthcare is a service organisation make a difference to how quality improvement is carried out?

5. QUALITY IMPROVEMENT APPROACHES

This section covers the major approaches to quality improvement that have been used in healthcare. Many of these have their roots in the work of the quality gurus (section 4.2) and some draw on similar principles to those of TQM (section 4.3), although the variety of definitions of TQM have led to a lack of clarity about exactly what constitutes many of these approaches.

We draw a distinction here between:

- **Approaches**: something promoted as a way of working – which may include a variety of different tools, sometimes to be used at specific points along a methodological 'roadmap'… They may be applied to the organisational system as a whole, and may also be applied to systems spanning organisations. Some people may come to regard an approach as merely a fad or label.

- **Tools**: techniques used for improvement which may be used alone, or in combination with others. More than one approach may suggest the use of the same tool.

Are tools useful on their own?

There is considerable debate about whether tools are of much value on their own, or whether they need to be deployed as part of a wider improvement **approach** across the organisation. Some argue that "teaching tools very rarely results in a change to the system" (Seddon 2005b) and certainly the notion that it is system issues which determine quality has a long history, from Deming (see section 4.2.1) to Don Berwick's application of these principles in healthcare (see section 3.1.3): *"The opportunities for improvement of quality lie in improved design of systems … I believe that this is also true of healthcare systems"* (Kenney 2008)

There is also debate about whether these approaches are really new, or just repackaging of existing concepts: *"Techniques touted as today's "core competencies" all too often become tomorrow's failed programs. However, digging a little deeper shows that many such techniques have useful content. It should come as little surprise then that many currently popular innovations are little more than old ideas with new acronyms. The core disciplines associated with statistical process control and variance reduction become six-sigma"* (Repenning & Sterman 2001, p.64). This review will attempt to identify where this has occurred.

Four aspects of each approach are considered:

- outline of the approach
- how the approach fits with others
- where the approach has been used in healthcare
- outcomes that have been reported.

5.1 The Plan-Do-Study-Act model

5.1.1 Outline of the approach

The plan-do-study-act (PDSA) model was developed by Deming (Deming 1986) – and termed by him the Shewhart cycle (Dale 2003). Deming's initial terminology was plan-do-check-act (PDCA), but he later changed this to PDSA to better reflect his thinking. PDSA is the term generally used in healthcare and which will therefore be used here.

The use of the PDSA is to improve processes and therefore outcomes (Deming 1986). Some view it simply as a problem-solving methodology (Pescod 1994), and others as part of a continuous improvement approach (Dale 2003). PDSA is very clearly a continuous improvement approach, rather than a breakthrough approach, and this may be in conflict with current management styles or past experience of improvement (Silvester, Lendon, Bevan et al. 2004).

PDSA appears to have been first formally proposed in healthcare by (Langley et al. 1996). The term "model for improvement" (Langley et al. 1996) (see Figure 1) is now also commonly used, and the text by Langley is regarded as the basis for much of what is now applied in healthcare in both the US and the UK. This links the PDSA cycle with three key questions (see Figure 1) and it is argued that it parallels learning developments and processes in education (Kolb 1984, Schon 1988).

Figure 1 – The Model for Improvement (Langley et al. 1996)

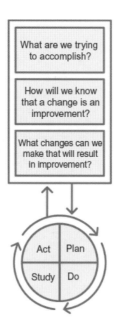

The use of this model over time to achieve improvement is often referred to as rapid-cycle improvement (Horton 2004), where a number of small PDSA cycles take place one after the other (see Figure 2).

Figure 2 - The Model for Improvement used over time (Schon 1988)

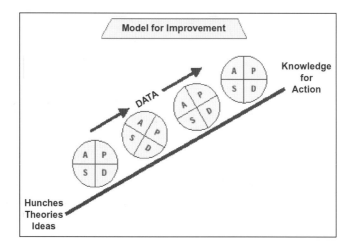

5.1.2   How the approach fits with others

There is no reference in the key text (Langley et al. 1996) to any other tools being a part of this approach. However, the notion of a change concept is relevant here. The model for improvement has developed into an approach rather than a tool and one which can be used as an overarching framework for other tools to be utilised.

Change Concepts ...

... can be defined as a *"general idea, with proven merit and sound scientific or logical foundation, that can stimulate specific ideas for changes that lead to improvement"* (Nolan & Schall 1996). They relate to the third question in the model – 'what changes can we make that will result in an improvement?' and are generally good ideas rather than specific ideas that are ready to be implemented, although there is a view that change concepts *"can be catalogued and made generally available to aid improvement work"* (Plsek 1999). A future development may be to grade the change concepts according to the evidence that underpins them (Plsek 1999), and it is argued that this lack of evidence to date has *"unnecessarily allowed critics of rapid cycle improvement to label the entire effort as unscientific (which it is not)"* (Plsek 1999). (Langley et al. 1996) describe 70 change concepts grouped into the categories of:

- eliminate waste

- improve work flow

- optimise inventory

- change the work environment

- enhance the product/customer relationship

- manage time

- manage variation

- design systems to avoid mistakes

- focus on a product/service

5.1.3 Where the approach has been used in healthcare: the collaborative approach

The improvement collaborative methodology was developed by the Institute of Healthcare Improvement in the US and is known as the 'breakthrough' model (Kilo 1998). This approach has since been adopted by a number of different countries in Europe, including England, Scotland, Wales, Sweden and France, to set up national system re-design initiatives for services such as cancer and coronary heart disease. The breakthrough improvement collaborative methodology derives from continuous quality improvement theories, combined with more general organisational theories of initiating, implementing, monitoring and evaluating change (i.e. the model for improvement). The approach involves a number of teams with a common interest (e.g. improving cancer services) working together in a structured way with a group of national experts for a period of around 12-18 months to plan, implement and monitor improvements in care. The basic building blocks of the approach include:

- generation of change concepts by an expert panel, based on existing evidence of best practice
- rapid cycle improvement, using the plan-do-study-act cycle
- a series of national learning events, followed by periods of local action and implementation
- ongoing communication and support from a team of national (and international) experts through regular conference calls and e-mail discussion groups
- regular feedback and comparison of data at a local and national level

Cancer Services Collaborative in England

The National Health Service (NHS) in England established a Cancer Services Collaborative in 1999, to improve the system of care delivery for patients with suspected or diagnosed cancer. Based on the IHI methodology, the Cancer Services Collaborative was underpinned by principles of system re-design and set out to challenge the way in which cancer services were organised around discrete departments and a perceived lack of awareness of the whole system of care. Since 1999, the initiative has progressed in three distinct phases. In each phase, the focus has been on the process of patient care from the point of referral through to diagnosis and treatment. The two key elements of redesign that have been introduced through the Collaborative focus on mapping the patient journey and addressing issues of capacity and demand.

Phase 1 ran from 1999 to 2001 and was set up as a pilot to identify what was actually happening to patients and what might be possible in terms of service re-design. 9 pilots in 8 of the 34 cancer networks[3] received central funding (around £500,000 per pilot site) to initiate improvements in one of five tumour group areas, namely, breast, lung, ovarian, prostate and colorectal cancer. In total, 51 clinical project teams were set up. Phase I of the Collaborative was evaluated by a research team from the University of Birmingham. The results of this evaluation study are discussed in section 5.1.4.

Phase 2 of the Collaborative took place from 2001 to 2003. The aim of this phase was to spread the Collaborative approach and methodology to all 34 of the cancer networks in England in order to establish what was possible and to identify examples of good practice. Further project teams were established and mandatory reporting of data on waiting times was introduced (Department of Health 2000), as part of the overall NHS performance management system. The establishment of the waiting time targets to be monitored was itself influenced by the findings from phase 1 of the Collaborative programme. By March 2003, the Modernisation Agency (MA) reported that through the Collaborative, they had worked with half of the 1600 specialist cancer teams in England. 28,000 changes had been tested (using the PDSA cycle), resulting in at least 2,800 improvements for cancer patients across England, including improved patient experiences, shorter waiting times, and more choice about treatment (NHS Modernisation Agency 2003).

Phase 3 of the collaborative was launched in March 2003 as the Cancer Services Collaborative – Improvement Partnership, again supported by central NHS funds (guaranteed until 2006). This phase focused on implementation and took a wider focus on all forms of cancer, alongside supporting services such as primary care, palliative care, radiotherapy, radiology, chemotherapy, endoscopy services, and patient and care experiences. As part of the developments, there was an explicit focus on integrating the work of primary care in the redesign of services.

---

3.   Following the publication of the Calman-Hine report on cancer services in 1995, 34 cancer networks were established throughout England to facilitate service planning and co-ordination of care across institutional boundaries.

5.1.4   Outcomes that have been reported

Although the methodology of improvement collaboratives has been adopted on a wide scale by health services across the world, there is little empirical evidence to suggest the approach is more cost-effective than other quality improvement methods (Øvretveit, Bate & Cleary 2002). A number of formal evaluations of improvement collaboratives have been reported. These demonstrate the impact of specific collaboratives on related outcomes such as:

- reduced infection rates in neonatal intensive care (Horbar, Rogowski & Plsek 2001)
- reduced caesarean section rates (Flamm, Berwick & Kabcenell 1998)
- reduced rates of adverse drug events (Leape, Kabcenell & Gandhi 2000).

However, questions have been raised at to whether the impact of collaboratives is as great as expected and significant differences in outcomes have been observed between different collaboratives and between different teams within the same collaborative (Bate, Robert & McLeod 2002).

Use of the PDSA model with NHS collaboratives has been reported (Kerr, Bevan, Gowland et al. 2002) to:

- facilitate the use of teamwork to make improvements
- provide a framework for the application of effective measurement and use of improvement tools
- encourage planning to be based on evidence-based theory
- emphasise and encourage learning
- provide a way to empower people to take action
- continue to create the will for improvement as tests of change are completed

The main evaluation in relation to the Cancer Service Collaborative in England (Robert, McLeod & Ham 2003) collected data from a wide range of sources, including collaborative participants and stakeholders, observation of meetings and conference calls, documentary evidence, cost data and patient level data on waiting times and booking. In terms of the impact of the collaborative, the views of staff were positive, especially in relation to changes in attitudes towards improvement, staff empowerment and the provision of time and training opportunities. However, experiences were seen to be highly context specific, with notable variations across and within programme sites. Most participants found the collaborative methodology useful, although some aspects of the approach were preferred over others. Participants were particularly negative about the volume of data monitoring and reporting required and generally raised questions about the processes of data collection and measurement, for example, in terms of the utility and validity of the measures used.

For some participants, the collaborative approach and the way it was presented through the training workshops was seen to be too theoretical, with too much jargon. Others felt the methodology was too prescriptive. This led the researchers to conclude that there was a very difficult balancing act to perform to get the right mix between the top-down, centralised structure of the programme and bottom up, local control of implementation (Robert et al. 2003).

In attempting to explain the variation in findings, the researchers highlight a number of process issues (defined as the key levers for change) that appeared to influence the outcome of the collaborative at a project team level. These include:

- the adoption of a patient perspective
- the availability of dedicated time
- opportunities for training
- facilitation of multi-disciplinary working
- staff empowerment
- opportunities for networking (Robert et al. 2003)

In turn, these were dependent on local leadership, the presence of clinical champions and wider organisational support for the collaborative. In their overall conclusions on the cancer services collaborative, the researchers highlight the importance of the so-called levers for change, alongside a receptive organisational context. Also the need to review measurement and reporting mechanisms and requirements within the collaborative methodology and to build in more preparatory work and the development of greater local ownership of the collaborative.

Another study which examined the effectiveness of collaboratives and the factors influencing this (Øvretveit et al. 2002) held structured discussions among researchers involved in evaluating collaboratives to consider three questions of effectiveness:

- are collaboratives effective or cost-effective?
- are the results sustained?
- can they be made more effective?

In response to the first question, the researchers noted that individual collaboratives had demonstrated an impact, but concluded that there is currently insufficient evidence to determine whether collaboratives are more or less cost-effective in making and spreading improvements than other approaches. By comparison to other approaches, collaboratives were seen to be expensive, because of the costs involved in holding several large-scale national meetings. Consequently, the issue of spread and sustainability was seen to be particularly important to justify the costs associated with collaboratives. However, longer-term evaluations to assess spread and sustainability are not yet available.

Features of collaboratives that were thought to be critical determinants of their effectiveness were examined by drawing on expert opinion and experiences of collaborative leaders (Wilson, Berwick & Cleary 2003). Seven key features were identified, and important characteristics of each of these dimensions are summarised in Table 3.

Table 3 - Determinants of the effectiveness of improvement collaboratives (Wilson et al. 2003)

Key Component	Common variations	Critical dimensions
Sponsorship	• government • professional organisations • independent quality organisations • non-profit and for-profit healthcare	• credibility of sponsor • perceived alignment with participants' values and aims • perceived gain for sponsors
Topic	• broad or narrow • complex or simple • alignment with local and national priorities	• consistency with local or national priorities • complexity • practical relevance • relative advantage • compatibility with current practices
Ideas for improvements	• inclusion or exclusion of practical knowledge • national or local experts • internal or external generation of knowledge • generic ideas for change or specific changes	• perceived validity of knowledge • applicability of knowledge locally • social distance between collaborative leaders and participants • amount of practical knowledge
Participants	• mandated or voluntary • pay vs. no pay • screening for previous improvement experience and readiness for change • multidisciplinary • inclusion of a medical clinician • team size • inclusion of team members directly affected by the change	• readiness for change • ability to work as a team • team size • heterogeneity of quality improvement experience
Senior leadership support	• variable support in form of resources and mission • praising and acknowledging improvement work	• support and resources for project
Preliminary work	• developing understanding of local system and its performance • occasional addition of extra learning sessions	• knowledge of local performance
Learning about and making improvements	• variable meetings for learning • methods for sharing; strong vs. weak sharing • reporting • rating system • collaborative size • use of improvement model • variable social interaction • different support mechanisms	• number of face-to-face meetings • total amount of inter-team contact • methods of information sharing used • improvement models/strategies used • ways of sharing good performance • strength of social and information networks • amount of central support

The findings from the research that have been reported to date highlight that collaboratives are complex, multi-faceted interventions. As such, it is unsurprising that there does not seem to be a right way of implementing a collaborative and that experience and outcomes vary considerably both across and within collaboratives. The key point seems to be tailoring implementation to match the specific healthcare, political or organisational context, depending on the particular collaborative and the reasons for its implementation. This requires some flexibility in the approach taken to designing and conducting improvement collaboratives to enable them to be more context-specific. Of particular importance seems to be an ability to get the right balance between top-down initiation and leadership of the collaborative and bottom-up ownership and commitment to the collaborative process.

Several evaluations highlight useful pointers that seem to be important in terms of maximising the effectiveness of collaboratives. These relate to the focus of the collaborative, the participants and their host organisation and the style and method of implementing the collaborative (Table 4).

Table 4 - Challenges for successful improvement collaboratives (Øvretveit et al. 2002)

Key Area	Challenge
Purpose and preparation	Choosing the right subject
	Ensuring participants define their objectives and assess their capacity to benefit from the collaborative
	Defining roles and making clear what is expected
	Ensuring team building and preparation by teams for the collaborative
Collaborative organisation and meetings	Enabling mutual learning rather than carrying out teaching
	Motivating and empowering teams
	Ensuring teams have measurable and achievable targets
	Equipping teams to deal with data and change challenges
Post-collaborative transition	Learning and planning for sustaining improvements
	Planning and learning for spread

Quality Improvement: Theory and Practice in Healthcare

Recent proposals and studies (Bate & Robert 2002) have suggested that rather than a collaborative approach, a community approach which better enables knowledge transfer would enable more effective learning and development, based around the concept of communities of practice (Wenger & Snyder 2000). Improvement collaboratives are based on many of the concepts of knowledge management (cross-boundary knowledge transfer, communal exchange of knowledge etc.), but it is argued (Bate & Robert 2002) that their impact could be strengthened if these concepts were developed further. In particular, they propose a more organic model of collaboratives, with less emphasis on rules, regulations and reporting relationships and a greater focus on people processes. In practice this would involve a greater emphasis on sharing tacit knowledge (know-how) alongside explicit knowledge (know-what), the creation, as well as the application, of knowledge, the development of more effective networks and the establishment of communities of practice, as opposed to time-limited project teams.

QUESTIONS TO THINK ABOUT:

Are there areas where the PDSA approach could be used in your organisation?
Where might a collaborative approach be beneficial in improving healthcare?

5.2 Statistical Process Control

5.2.1 Outline of the approach

The roots of Statistical Process Control (SPC) can be traced to work in the 1920s in Bell Laboratories (Shewhart 1931), where Shewhart sought to identify the difference between natural variation – termed 'common cause' - and that which could be controlled – 'special' or 'assignable' cause variation. Processes that exhibited only common cause variation were said to be in statistical control. One of the many significant features of this work, which is still used in basically the same form today, is *"the management of quality acquired a scientific and statistical foundation"* (Kolesar 1993).

The central tool is the control chart, which adds process variation bounds (typically at ±2 or 3 standard deviations) to the simple time-sequence of a run chart. These bounds are referred to as upper and lower control limits. Target or specification limits are usually not plotted when the charts are used by process operators to avoid compromising achievable performance (Pyzdek 2003a). As an approach, SPC uses control charts (typically in pairs recording the evolution of both level and variation over time) to identify potential for process improvement (eliminating special causes and reducing common cause variation) and to monitor a process in real time in order to detect deteriorating performance (importantly seeking to identify trends and so pre-empt unacceptable 'out of control' performance).

Figure 3 - Example c-chart using number of emergency admissions on consecutive Mondays (Mohammed, Worthington & Woodall 2008)

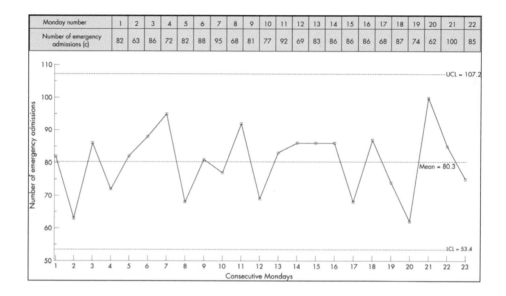

Monday number	1	2	3	4	5	6	7	8	9	10	11	12	13	14	15	16	17	18	19	20	21	22
Number of emergency admissions (c)	82	63	86	72	82	88	95	68	81	77	92	69	83	86	86	86	68	87	74	62	100	85

5.2.2   How the approach fits with others

Aside from the use that was made of SPC by Deming etc, the 1980s saw a revival in its use as TQM concepts developed from the work of the original quality gurus (Dale 2003). It is usually regarded as a tool for measurement (Plsek 1999) within a wider approach, rather than as an overall approach in it own right. For example:

- it is an important part of the final (control) stage of the Six Sigma Define-Measure-Analyse-Improve-Control (DMAIC) roadmap (see section 5.3.1)

- it provides a key problem-identification tool at the start of the Decalogue approach to the Theory of Constraints (ToC) (see section 5.5.1)

- it can also support the analysis and interpretation of data, for example as part of the check or study stage of the PDSA cycle

Though use of SPC has grown at a relatively rapid rate, growth may have been even more rapid if SPC did not challenge many of the fundamental assumptions in healthcare about how to deliver improvement - in the same way that Deming's approach does (Mohammed 2004) - in particular the focus on short-term cost reduction. In another paper the same author suggests that SPC is superior to tools more commonly used to analyse variation in healthcare because it provides guidance for action: "we should seriously question the role of conventional statistical analysis in clinical governance" (Mohammed, Cheng, Rouse et al. 2001).

5.2.3   Where the approach has been used in healthcare

The recognition of the importance of variation in healthcare (e.g. Haraden & Resar 2004, Proudlove, Black & Fletcher 2007, Walley, Silvester, Steyn et al. 2006b), has naturally led to an interest in SPC (Berwick 1991).

- a systematic review of the use of SPC in healthcare (Thor, Lundberg, Ask et al. 2007) found a wide range of applications, from clinical and resource management through biomedical variables (including by self-managing patients) to patient experience. The earliest papers they identified were US applications in 1990 and from 1998 elsewhere

- clinical applications, including laboratory results, medication errors and application at individual patient level are discussed by (Plsek 1999)

- a systematic review of the use of SPC in patient monitoring concluded that the four 'gold standard' studies found showed *"control charts to be simple, low-cost, effective tools with good sensitivity and specificity characteristics"* (Tennant, Mohammed, Coleman et al. 2007). The four case-study reports also reported positive impact on quality of care, patient experience and carer experience

- the use of SPC is debated (Benneyan & Kaminsky 1995)

- some of the more methodologically robust papers about SPC application include (Benneyan, Lloyd & Plsek 2003) and (Marshall, Mohammed & Rouse 2004)

- the profile of SPC amongst UK doctors was raised by the widely publicised application to data about mortality in the light of the Shipman case and the Bristol enquiry (Mohammed et al. 2001, Mohammed, Rathbone, Myers et al. 2004)

In the US the use of SPC has been encouraged by the IHI and other improvement specialists (Carey 2002)[4] and the NHS picked up on this (Balestracci 1998), as part of the Improvement Partnership for Hospitals initiative (NHS Institute for Innovation and Improvement & Matrix Research and Consultancy 2006).

As a result, an Excel-based SPC tool was widely distributed in the NHS and appears to be used in places. In particular, control charts are used to display performance over time and assess the impact of interventions, (e.g. Walley, Silvester & Mountford 2006a). Some NHS trusts now use control or run chart format to present hospital-level activity reports and courses have been run to help board-level managers interpret such charts. Guidance for healthcare practitioners on how to use control charts has also been made generally available (Mohammed et al. 2008).

---

4   SPC is not however featured as a discrete theme in the work of the IHI although control charts are widely used in a number of their work areas

5.2.4   Outcomes that have been reported

Lists of benefits, limitations, barriers and facilitating conditions for SPC in healthcare were shown by a systematic review (Thor et al. 2007) and included:

- improving communication between clinicians, managers and patients by providing a shared language
- describing and quantifying variation
- identifying areas for potential improvement
- assessing the impact of change interventions

A study of the effect of presenting data as league tables vs. control charts, for the purposes of decision-making concluded that fewer outliers for further investigation are identified when data is presented in control charts (Marshall et al. 2004).

Use of SPC to link performance information to physician compensation and practice management has been shown to improve financial performance (Stewart, Greisler & Feldman 2002).

A series of examples presented which, though it is not clear how closely they are based on real cases, show that using SPC enables teams to decide on the most appropriate improvement strategy: searching for special causes or more fundamental process redesign (Benneyan, Lloyd & Plsek 2004).

Issues in using SPC, and the thinking behind it, highlighted by applications in healthcare include:

- the limitations to the objective being reduction of variation (McLaughlin 1996, Seddon 2005a)
- the complexity and appropriateness of data sets representing aggregations of different types of patients or management units (Thor et al. 2007)
- the implications on the underlying statistics of having very small or very large data sets (Mohammed & Laney 2006)

QUESTIONS TO THINK ABOUT:

Where could SPC be used in your organisation for presenting and monitoring clinical and non-clinical data?
What awareness of variation and its effects do you have within the organisation?

5.3 Six Sigma

5.3.1 Outline of the approach

Six Sigma is a process or product improvement or (re)design approach developed initially by Motorola in the 1980s, then further by Allied Signal and General Electric. Having achieved widespread acceptance in manufacturing, Six Sigma is becoming popular in the service sector especially with US-owned firms (Schroeder, Linderman, Liedtke et al. 2007).

History of Six Sigma (developed from Laux 2008)

The roots of Six Sigma as a measurement standard can be traced back to Carl Frederick Gauss (1777-1855) who introduced the concept of the normal curve. Six Sigma as a measurement standard in product variation can be traced back to the 1920s when Walter Shewhart showed that three sigma [three standard deviations (SDs)] from the mean is the point where a process requires correction. Many measurement standards later came on the scene but credit for coining the term Six Sigma goes to a Motorola engineer named Bill Smith (Six Sigma is a federally registered trademark of Motorola).

In the late 1970s, Dr Mikel Harry, a senior staff engineer at Motorola's Government Electronics Group (GEG) began to experiment with problem solving through statistical analysis. Using his methodology, GEG began to show dramatic results – GEG's products were being designed and produced faster and more cheaply. Subsequently, Dr. Harry began to formulate a method for applying Six Sigma throughout Motorola. His work culminated in a paper titled "The Strategic Vision for Accelerating Six Sigma within Motorola." He was later appointed head of the Motorola Six Sigma Research Institute and became the driving force behind Six Sigma.

Dr Mikel Harry and Richard Schroeder, an ex-Motorola executive, were responsible for creating the unique combination of change management and data-driven methodologies that transformed Six Sigma from a simple quality measurement tool to the breakthrough business excellence philosophy it is today. They had the charisma and the ability to educate and engage business leaders such as Bob Galvin of Motorola, Larry Bossidy of AlliedSignal (now Honeywell), and Jack Welch of GE. Together, Harry and Schroeder elevated Six Sigma from the shop floor to the boardroom with their drive and innovative ideas regarding entitlement, breakthrough strategy, sigma levels, and the roles for deployment of Black Belts, Master Black Belts and Champions.

How is Six Sigma defined?

There are various understandings of what Six Sigma is (Proudlove and Boaden 2006b, Schroeder, Linderman, Liedtke et al, 2007), though most authors agree it builds on the work of Shewart and Deming and the Total Quality Management (TQM) approach. Six Sigma has not been carefully defined in either the practitioner or academic literature but a comprehensive definition which is well accepted is:

> "Six Sigma is an organized and systematic method for strategic process improvement and new product and service development that relies on statistical methods and the scientific method to make dramatic reductions in customer defined defect rates (Linderman, Schroeder, Zaheer et al. 2003 p.195)

This definition highlights the importance of improvements based on the customer's definition of a defect. A key step in any Six Sigma improvement effort is determining exactly what the customer requires and then defining defects in terms of their 'critical to quality' parameters. Many argue that Six Sigma is "a tactical methodology to determine the best approach for a given situation/process" and that it "should not be considered just another initiative but should integrate other programs … as part of an overall business strategy" (Breyfogle III, Cupello & Meadows 2001).

What does the term 'Six Sigma' mean?

Six Sigma enabled Motorola to express its quality goal as 3.4 defects per million opportunities (DPMO), where a defect opportunity is a process output that fails to meet the customer's critical requirements. Motorola set the goal to be reducing the SD of a process so that the distance from the process target setting (mean) to the (nearest) defect threshold would be 6 SDs (Breyfogle III et al. 2001). They further assumed that the process was subject to disturbances that could cause the process mean to drift over time by as much as 1.5 SD from the target setting (Montgomery 2001), which then results in the distance being 4.5 SD and so (from the normal probability distribution) to the defect rate being 3.4 DPMO. This goal was far beyond normal quality levels and required very aggressive improvement efforts.

Quality Improvement: Theory and Practice in Healthcare

The full Six Sigma approach can be considered to consist of the following elements (Proudlove & Boaden 2006b):

a. An underlying philosophy

This is to define acceptable process output according to the customer's measure of quality, then reduce process variation on this measure by establishing (statistically if possible) root causes of variation.

b. Underpinning elements

These focus on deployment, support and training infrastructure (including 'belt' certification structure: see Table 5). A major deployment of Six Sigma involves training and coaching by very experienced Master Black Belts (MBBs) of practitioners (typically Green Belts (GBs)) and expert practitioners (Black Belts (BBs)) who undertake improvement projects with the support of Champions (leaders and senior managers who ensure that resources are available for training and projects, and who are involved in project progress reviews).

Table 5 – Six sigma levels of certification[5]

Master Black Belt	Master Black Belts are Six Sigma quality experts who are responsible for the strategic implementations within an organisation. Master Black Belt's main responsibilities include training and mentoring of Black Belts and Green Belts; helping to prioritise, select and charter high-impact projects; maintaining the integrity of the Six Sigma measurements, improvements and tollgates; and developing, maintaining and revising Six Sigma training materials.
Black Belt	Six Sigma team leaders are responsible for implementing process improvement projects within the business — to increase customer satisfaction levels and business productivity. Black Belts are knowledgeable and skilled in the use of the Six Sigma methodology and tools. Black Belts have typically completed four weeks of Six Sigma training, and have demonstrated mastery of the subject matter through the completion of project(s) and an examination. Black Belts coach Green Belts and receive coaching and support from Master Black Belts.
Green Belt	An employee of an organization who has been trained on the improvement methodology of Six Sigma and will lead a process improvement or quality improvement team as part of their full time job. Their degree of knowledge and skills associated with Six Sigma is less than that of a Black Belt or Master Black Belt. Extensive product knowledge in their company is a must in their task of process improvement. The Green Belt employee plays an important role in executing the Six Sigma process at an organisation level.

5.   http://www.isixsigma.com/dictionary

c. Methodologies or roadmaps

These guide practitioners through problem solving steps, providing structure for using tools. Six Sigma uses a structured method, whether the task is process improvement or new product design.

- In the case of process improvement, define, measure, analyze, improve and control (DMAIC) are used as the five steps in process improvement.
- Somewhat different roadmaps called Design for Six Sigma (DFSS) are used for radical or incremental product design (e.g. define, measure, analyse, design and verify (DMADV)). These are less frequently used than DMAIC and use more complex statistical tools, so are usually supported by more experienced practitioners.

The main steps in DMAIC are illustrated in Figure 4. Since the use of DMAIC is dominant it is sometimes mistakenly taken to be synonymous with Six Sigma.

Figure 4 - The main steps in DMAIC (Brassard, Finn, Ginn et al. 2002).

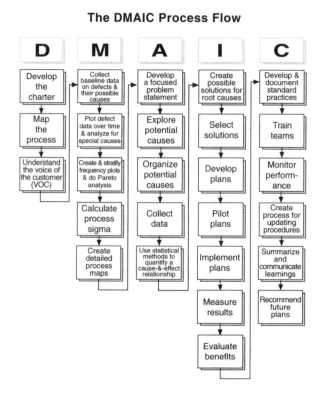

The DMAIC Process Flow

D	M	A	I	C
Develop the charter	Collect baseline data on defects & their possible causes	Develop a focused problem statement	Create possible solutions for root causes	Develop & document standard practices
Map the process	Plot defect data over time & analyze for special causes	Explore potential causes	Select solutions	Train teams
Understand the voice of the customer (VOC)	Create & stratify frequency plots & do Pareto analysis	Organize potential causes	Develop plans	Monitor performance
	Calculate process sigma	Collect data	Pilot plans	Create process for updating procedures
	Create detailed process maps	Use statistical methods to quantify a cause-&-effect relationship	Implement plans	Summarize and communicate learnings
			Measure results	Recommend future plans
			Evaluate benefits	

d. A large toolkit

This includes process mapping and SPC – see (Pyzdek 2003b) for a comprehensive guide to the tools. There is a careful integration of the tools with the overall method: *"Whatever method is chosen …it is important that the method be carefully followed and a solution not offered until the problem is clearly defined. Data and objective measurement is critical at each step of the method. The standard statistical quality tools are incorporated into the structured method as needed … this careful integration of tools with the methods is unique to Six Sigma."* (Linderman et al. 2003, p.195).

Is Six Sigma a new approach?

Debate about whether Six Sigma is really new, when it has been around since the mid-1980s is in one sense irrelevant. However, there are clearly a variety of schools of thought about what Six Sigma is, from *"a set of historically known and used statistical techniques, in a new package"* (Breyfogle III et al. 2001, Klefsjö, Wiklund & Edgeman 2001) to *"an effective application of statistical techniques, delivered in an innovative manner that has achieved acceptance, use and results by the management of many organisations"* (Breyfogle III et al. 2001, Harry & Schroeder 1999).

Many authors claim that it is not new (Klefsjö et al. 2001), and justify their views by tracing back the emphasis on process and variation to both Deming (Deming 1986) and Shewhart (Shewhart 1931). Others claim (George & Rowlands 2003) that it has borrowed from the best of Deming and adds features like a comprehensive training structure and a broad definition of value from a customer perspective, which includes quality but also service and delivery.

Perhaps what is new is the explicit linking of the tactical and the strategic – where statistical techniques are *"used in a systematic way … there is a focus on results, including customer-related ones that lead to enhanced marketplace performance"* (Klefsjö et al. 2001). It could be suggested that it is therefore the use of Six Sigma as an overall approach rather than simply the tools which is new.

The contribution of both the underpinnings (that support and drive change capability) and the DMAIC methodology (which provides rigour and a logical structure to guide tool use) are highlighted by some authors (Proudlove & Boaden 2006b). Others (Schroeder et al. 2007) identify the key strength and differentiator of Six Sigma to be the underpinnings, which they characterise as creating a very strong improvement structure (a 'meso-structure') in parallel with the management hierarchy in an organisation. However they only examined comprehensive deployments of Six Sigma in large organisations. Additional views come from a review of Six Sigma, where two important features are described: *"building and maintaining management support and fostering use of methods among practitioners who are not experts in statistics"* (Brady & Allen 2006).

5.3.2   How the approach fits with others

Many organisations claiming success in Six Sigma also have long-established TQM programmes (McAdam & Lafferty 2004), and some appear to re-label their TQM programmes as Six Sigma. Others do not view it as an alternative to TQM, but one approach that supports the principles of TQM – in this case, a methodology within TQM, likened to Business Process Reengineering (Klefsjö et al. 2001).

Others have claimed that Six Sigma is a more analytical and data-based approach than TQM, or at least as it appeared to be practised, *"little more than an ill-defined motivation or culture change programme"* (Bicheno 2002). A further comparison is made by (Lazarus 2003) – see Table 6.

Table 6 - TQM and Six Sigma (Lazarus 2003)

TQM	Six Sigma
Typically grass-roots driven	Top-down implementation
Incremental improvement i.e. 10-15%	Breakthrough improvement i.e. 50-100%
Focus is ongoing	Focus is short-term projects
Goal is 'more with more' i.e. inspection	Focus is 'more with less'
Consensus driven	Data driven, using statistical analysis

The comparison made more recently between Six Sigma and Lean will be covered in section 5.4.2, following the description of Lean.

5.3.3   Where the approach has been used in healthcare

A key early reference on Six Sigma in healthcare considered the implications of translating Six Sigma (as an approach for reducing error and improving reliability) into healthcare from a conceptual position (Chassin 1998), concluding that it is possible and the journey should start. However, the reference is US-focused, as is a more recent overview, which includes a list of examples and a case study (Sehwail & DeYong 2003).

A key US author is Revere (Black & Revere 2006, Revere & Black 2003, Revere, Black & Huq 2004) who looked at the implications of Six Sigma for patient care in a general sense, in conjunction with Continuous Quality Improvement (CQI) approaches - including a review of areas where it has been applied - and on use of Six Sigma in medication (Chaplin 2003). Other areas which feature in the literature include radiology (Benedetto 2003a, Benedetto 2003b), nursing (Lanham & Maxson-Cooper 2003) and pharmacy (Johnstone, Hendrickson, Derbach et al. 2003). Most of these appear to assume that Six Sigma can be applied in healthcare and then simply go on to describe how.

Many other papers are essentially trade journal descriptions of the implementation of Six Sigma with little real analysis of the problems/issues of translation (Anonymous 2000, 2003, Brantes & Galvin 2001, Buck 1998, Grazier 2003, Grim 2001, Lazarus 2003, Lazarus & Stamps 2002, Lucier & Seshadri 2001, Scalise 2003, Simmons 2002, Snee 2000, Thomerson 2001, 2002, Thomson & Lewis 2002). Others are merely proposals for use (Frings & Grant 2005).

There are various books on Six Sigma in healthcare including:

- one described by the authors as 'jargon free' and without an academic focus (Barry, Murcko & Brubaker 2002)
- one written by authors who wrote earlier papers and 'how to' books on the topic in manufacturing, and who are both practitioners rather than academics (Snee & Hoerl 2004)
- one published by the American Society for Quality, intended for senior managers of hospitals and medical clinics (Barry & Smith 2005)

A paper considering how to win the support of clinicians for Six Sigma postulates that the fact that Six Sigma is quantitative, based on "solid data carefully validated for accuracy" and able to achieve lasting results will attract clinicians to this method (Ettinger & Kooy 2003). Their description of the process by which clinicians respond to Six Sigma is as follows (Ettinger & Kooy 2003):

- they challenge the data as usual
- when their initial objections are addressed, they take a more focused approach to questioning the quality of the data
- when the data stands up again, they sit up a bit and dust off their methodological training. They ask a few more pointed questions about the methodology, see that it is sound and then a transformation takes place

These accounts are overwhelmingly US-based, though some application has been made in at least one Irish hospital (presented at practitioner conferences only) and major use at a hospital in the Netherlands has been formally reported (van den Heuvel, Does & Verver 2005).

Application within the NHS

In the NHS, reports of attempts to implement Six Sigma go back to the early 1990s (Merry & Wing 1993). A recent paper claims that Six Sigma is the 'cure' for the NHS and predicted that use of Six Sigma "will continue to grow, especially here in the UK over the next five years" although the paper makes no reference to any recent or current use within the NHS (Antony, Downey-Ennis, Antony et al. 2007b). They further predict use of DFSS for designing new processes and products in services.

Some training in Six Sigma was provided to the NHS in 2004-5, the details of which are given below. The learning from this has also been published (Proudlove et al. 2008).

Training for Six Sigma in the NHS

The NHS Modernisation Agency (MA) ran a major experiment with Six Sigma in England in 2004-05; the Green Belt programme, with over 50 staff participating in two four-day periods of training, whilst working on projects in 14 teams. The training and project coaching was led by Juran Institute MBBs with support from two NHS staff who had previously achieved BB level. The projects involved both primary and secondary care, and activities from A&E to outpatients. The programme was observed and evaluated for the NHS MA by a team from Manchester Business School (MBS) (Proudlove et al. 2008).

Separately, a Welsh multi-hospital trust has trained up some staff to be BBs and has been using Six Sigma - alongside Lean tools (in particular value stream mapping (VSM)) - for many years (Esain, Angel & Robertson 2006).

5.3.4 Outcomes that have been reported

There are numerous accounts of positive business outcomes from the use of Six Sigma in manufacturing (Hutchins 2000) but these have generally not been independently evaluated (Ferlie, Aggarwal & McGivern 2002). In general, the academic literature on Six Sigma is descriptive, with a *"paucity of studies that fundamentally critique the phenomena of Six Sigma in organisations from both people and process perspectives"* (Erwin & Douglas 2000).

A review of Six Sigma from an academic perspective (Antony 2004), highlights that the academic perspective on Six Sigma is lagging behind the practice and that a theoretical underpinning is currently lacking, something also supported by Linderman et al. 2003. Another review notes a shifting interest from practitioners towards academics (Brady & Allen 2006). Comprehensive reviews of the general literature on Six Sigma (Hendry & Nonthaleerak 2005, Nonthaleerak & Hendry 2006) conclude that, despite the great claims made for it, so far there is little rigorous empirical evidence for financial returns or on enablers and barriers to success.

Success factors such as leadership and top management commitment are listed by many authors (Antony, Antony, Kumar et al. 2007a, Banuelas & Antony 2002, Brady & Allen 2006), but not investigated using rigorous methodology.

Given the relatively unobjective accounts of Six Sigma in healthcare published to date it is not possible to give independent views on the reported outcomes. However, it is worth listing some of the outcomes described (Table 7). Many other examples of Six Sigma projects with positive outcomes in US hospitals can also be found (Antony et al. 2007b). It is noted that *"Six Sigma has not been widely applied to patient care"* (Revere et al. 2004), a conclusion supported by the data in Table 7. There are undoubtedly other narrative examples of the application of Six Sigma in healthcare, but no accounts of independent evaluation have been found.

Table 7 – Outcomes from applying Six Sigma in healthcare

Organisation (reference)	Outcomes reported
Commonwealth Health Corporation (CHC) (Simmons 2002)	• greater efficiency in radiology – cost per procedure reduced by 21.5% • throughput increased by 25% • changing culture and understanding a data approach also reported
Long Island Jewish (LIJ) Health System (Cooper 2002, Scalise 2003, Simmons 2002)	• improved billing accuracy saved over a quarter of a million dollars a year, reduced bed turnaround time by 50% and emergency wait time by 25%
Froedtert Memorial Lutheran Hospital (Lanham & Maxson-Cooper 2003, Simmons 2002)	• lab sample transport system speeded up and errors reduced by 35%
Charleston Area Medical Center (CAMC) (Revere et al. 2004, Simmons 2002)	• speeded up employee recruitment, saving money on overtime • improved supply chain for surgical supplies, saving over half a million dollars
Virtual Health (Ettinger 2001, Scalise 2003, Simmons 2002)	• did nine projects, saving over $4m on an investment of $1.4m
McLeod Regional Medical Centre (Scalise 2003)	• reduced service time in registration by 25%, and reduced patient and physician complaints
Mount Carmel Health (Revere et al. 2004)	• refined patient coding and saved over $800,000
Scottsdale Health Care (Revere et al. 2004)	• reduced time to transfer emergency patient to a bed, saved $600,000
Bon Secours Health System (Swayne 2003)	• many examples, including reduction in nurse overtime of 65% due to more effective patient placement
Sentara Healthcare (Swayne 2003)	• reduced ventilation stay of 25%, defects per million reduced by 12%
Red Cross Hospital (the Netherlands) (van den Heuvel et al. 2005)	• saved €1.2 million per year from 21 finished projects, expect to save €3 million per year from 23 running projects
Red Cross Hospital (the Netherlands) – Lean Six Sigma (de Koning, Verver, van den Heuvel et al. 2006)	• personnel hiring savings €36,000 (target); OT reduced delayed starts; maintenance savings €200,000 (achieved)

Outcomes of the Six Sigma training in the NHS

The outcomes of the NHS Green Belt experiment (Proudlove et al. 2008) show that:

- Many processes were unready for Six Sigma, or at least for DMAIC process improvement (being ill-defined or chaotic). This experience then contributed to subsequent NHS interest in Lean Six Sigma and (pure) Lean approaches (see section 5.4.3)

- The DMAIC approach, and its associated tools, was very rigorous, and particularly valuable at the Define and Measure phases in finding out the customer point of view, thinking hard about what the process is, measuring how it is performing and obtaining evidence for root causes

- However, rigour came at the cost of very considerable effort and (at the time) frustration, and required considerable coaching to maintain both thoroughness and project momentum.

More general findings, applicable to all improvement projects included:

- Project selection, and linking projects to important organisational goals is important
- Jargon can be off-putting
- In the NHS, identifying customers and processes can seem particularly difficult.

During use in Wales (Esain et al. 2006) it was noted that the customer focus tools in the 'Define' phase were considered stronger and more robust than others used, and that the rigour of the DMAIC process was important. They also conclude that expressing project outcome in terms of cost is *"not a motivational concept for improvement"*. In the NHS context, greater throughput may often be more immediate to many staff than the cost savings emphasised in US and Dutch deployments of Six Sigma.

QUESTIONS TO THINK ABOUT:

Does the fact that use of Six Sigma as an overall approach requires understanding of statistical tools make it inappropriate for use in the NHS?

Are there areas where a structured approach to problem-solving would be beneficial - for example, using the DMAIC roadmap without some or any of the recommended tools?

Is your process ready for improvement (is it stable and definable), or does it need redesign first?

Do you have coaches available who can support the rigour of an improvement project and advise on appropriate tools?

5.4 Lean

5.4.1 Outline of the approach

The term Lean has been developed in the context of manufacturing from the way in which Toyota, and other Japanese motor manufacturers, organise their production processes. Much of the original work with Toyota was carried out by Ohno (Ohno & (translator) Rosen 1995).

Recent authors have attempted to summarise how Toyota works although some argue (Spear & Bowen 1999) that many of the practices used by Toyota have been studied but *"the essence of Toyota's system consists of tacit knowledge, and is so woven into the culture, not written down, and workers could not articulate it"* (Jimmerson, Weber & Sobek 2005, p.5). However, the two accounts of the Toyota Production System (TPS) most often used in the West are:

The Machine that Changed the World

The term Lean production was coined by the authors of the book *The Machine that Changed the World* in 1990 (Womack, Jones & Roos 1990). Lean production was then seen to consist of Lean manufacturing, Lean product development, supply chain coordination, customer distribution and Lean enterprise management (Womack et al. 1990).

Over the early 1990s these principles were gradually extended from the shop floor to other areas and other industries, so that system design was described as based on *"Lean principles"* (Womack & Jones 1996). It is argued that this may have happened as a reaction against a 'one best way' approach, *"where advocates of Lean thinking started to re-position Lean thinking as based on a set of five key principles that it was claimed could be applied across a wide range of industrial settings"* (Hines, Holweg & Rich 2004). Although many of the examples were based on manufacturing industries and involved the common application of kaikaku (improvement via breakthrough events, as opposed to kaizen, continuous improvement).

The five Lean principles articulated by these authors are:
- the identification of customer value
- the management of the value stream
- developing the capability to flow production
- the use of 'pull' mechanisms to support material flow
- the pursuit of perfection through reducing all forms of waste in the system

These principles are also described as the "essential implementation sequence" for Lean [6] i.e. the steps that organisations should follow in order to become Lean.

The Toyota Way

A series of books by Jeffrey Liker (Liker 2004) describe the way in which Toyota works as the Toyota Production System (TPS). This is summarised in Figure 5:

Figure 5 – The Toyota Way

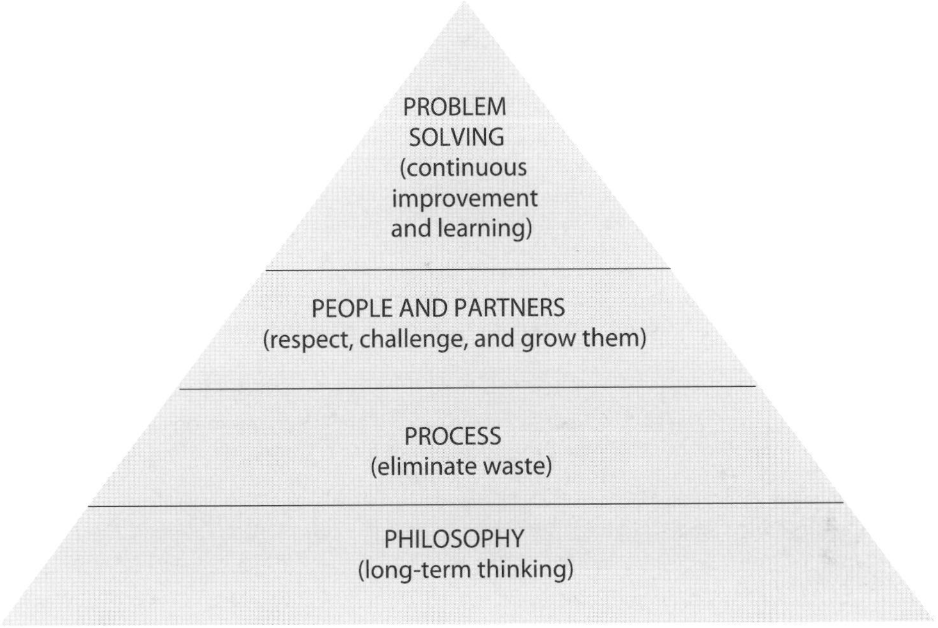

PROBLEM
SOLVING
(continuous
improvement
and learning)

PEOPLE AND PARTNERS
(respect, challenge, and grow them)

PROCESS
(eliminate waste)

PHILOSOPHY
(long-term thinking)

The problem-solving element of this is seen as key to success: *"they tightly couple the process of doing work with the process of learning to do it better as it's being done. Operations are expressly designed to reveal problems as they occur. When they arise, no matter how trivial they are, they are addressed quickly, If the solution … generates new insights, these are deployed systematically"* (Spear 2005).

The TPS is summarised as *"Toyota's real achievement is not merely the creation and use of the tools themselves; it is in making all its work a series of nested, on-going experiments"* (Spear 2004, p.79). The same author is clear that the TPS is about applying principles rather than tools – which is why it is so difficult to emulate. This approach is summarised in Table 8 (Liker 2004).

6.   http://www.lean.org/WhatsLean/CommonLeanQuestions.cfm

Table 8 – Delivering Operational Excellence: the Toyota Production System

Delivering Operational Excellence

Four basic organisational capabilities, if properly developed and nurtured, deliver the kind of operational excellence exhibited at Toyota and companies like it:

1. Work is designed as a series of ongoing experiments that immediately reveal problems, in order to drive out any ambiguity, employees in industry-leading companies spell out how work is expected to proceed in extraordinary detail, especially for highly complex and idiosyncratic processes. This increases the chance that the employees will succeed because it forces them to make their best understanding of a process explicit. If they don't succeed, spelling out what is expected increases the chance that problems will be detected earlier rather than later, since people will be surprised by the unexpected outcome. Such companies go even further by embedding tests into the work that show when what is actually happening is contrary to what was expected.
2. Problems are addressed immediately through rapid experimentation. When something does not go as expected, the problem is not worked around. Instead, it is addressed by those most affected by its ramifications, contained and prevented from propagating and corrupting someone else's work. Causes are quickly investigated and countermeasures rapidly tested to prevent the problem from recurring. When those who first address a problem are flummoxed, the problem is quickly escalated up the hierarchy so that broader perspectives and additional resources are brought to its resolution.
3. Solutions are disseminated adaptively through collaborative experimentation. When an effective countermeasure is developed, its use is not limited to where It has been discovered. But that doesn't mean the countermeasure is simply rolled out as a cookie cutter solution. Rather, people build on local insights into reducing defects, improving safety, enhancing responsiveness, and increasing efficiency by solving problems with colleagues from other disciplines and areas so that the countermeasure, and the process by which it was developed, is made explicit, can be emulated, and can be critiqued.
4. People at all levels of the organization are taught to become experimentalists. Finally, managers at companies like Toyota don't pretend that the ability to design work carefully, improve processes and transfer knowledge about those improvements develops automatically or easily. Coaching, mentoring, training and assisting activities constantly cascade down to ever more junior workers, thereby building exceptionally adaptive and self-renewing organisations.

The tools associated with a Lean approach

Like many other approaches Lean consists of a number of tools, some of which are also used in other approaches to improvement. Some authors give more extensive lists of tools which may be used within a Lean approach based on wider literature reviews (Bicheno 2000). A comparison of the tools which might constitute Lean, with a focus on healthcare, from a variety of sources is given in Table 9.

Table 9 – Tools associated with a Lean approach

Literature review (Bhasin & Burcher 2006)	Empirical Review of Lean in the public sector (Radnor, Walley, Stephens et al. 2006)	NHS Institute for Innovation and Improvement (NHS Institute for Innovation and Improvement 2007)	Lean tools in the Virginia Mason Production System (Nelson-Peterson & Leppa 2007)	Lean tools in healthcare (Manos, Sattler & Alukal 2006)
Continuous improvement/ kaizen	Rapid Improvement Events (RIEs or Kaizen Blitz)	RIEs		
Cellular manufacturing	Less commonly used		U-shaped cells	Cellular
Kanban (pull) system		Pull signals	Kanban	Pull systems
JIT			JIT	JIT
Single piece flow			One piece flow	Batch size reduction
Process mapping	Process mapping (sometimes as Value Steam Mapping, VSM)	VSM		VSM
Single minute exchange of dies (SMED) i.e. reduction of changeover time				Quick changeover
Step change/Kaikaku				
Supplier development				
Supplier base reduction				
5S and general visual management	5S	Visual workplace/5S	Visual control	5S workplace organisation Visual workplace systems
Total productive maintenance (TPM)	Less commonly used			TPM
The seven wastes	Identification and eliminating of waste			

Table 9 – Tools associated with a Lean approach - continued...

Literature review (Bhasin & Burcher 2006)	Empirical Review of Lean in the public sector (Radnor, Walley, Stephens et al. 2006)	NHS Institute for Innovation and Improvement (NHS Institute for Innovation and Improvement 2007)	Lean tools in the Virginia Mason Production System (Nelson-Peterson & Leppa 2007)	Lean tools in healthcare (Manos, Sattler & Alukal 2006)
	Market-based demand analysis			
	Work standardisation (less commonly used)	Work standardisation	Standard work and cycle times	Standardised work
		Staff involvement		
		Multi-functional staff		
		Match resources to demand		
				Point of use storage
				Poka-yoke (mistake proofing)
				Self inspection
				Autonomation – automation with a human touch

It should be noted that there is no definitive list of tools which comprise the Lean approach, with some authors arguing (Hines et al. 2004) that *"from a strategic point of view however, you can integrate other approaches (particularly the tools they offer) without contradicting the core objective of Lean – to provide customer value. In other words, any concept that provides customer value can be in line with a Lean strategy, even if Lean production tools on the shop-floor, such as Kanban, level scheduling, or take time, are not used"* (p.1006).

Tools commonly used

Of the wide variety of tools available, the main ones used within the public sector appear to be value stream mapping (VSM)/process mapping, 5S and kaizen blitz/rapid improvement events (RIEs). Although there is little formal research to support this view, there is plenty of informal and anecdotal evidence, not least the number of training programmes now available for these approaches.

Value Stream Mapping

VSM (Hines & Rich 1997) enables the seven common 'wastes' identified in the Toyota Production system to then be addressed by some combination of other Lean tools. In addition to the conventional mapping of activities, VSM adds an assessment of whether each activity is value-adding or waste.

Table 10 – The seven wastes

Overproduction
Waiting
Transport
Inappropriate processing
Unnecessary inventory
Unnecessary motion
Defects

5S

5S *"is the basic housekeeping discipline for Lean, quality and safety"* Bicheno (2004: p.52). There are various labels for each of the five S's, but the thinking is the same:

1. Sort - classify equipment and supplies by frequency of use, remove what is not used

2. Simplify/Straighten/Set in order - allocate a place for equipment and supplies, standardise locations with labelling, shadow boards, inventory footprints etc

3. Shine/Scrub - clean and check

4. Standardise/Stabilise - adopt standard work and standards for 5S

5. Sustain/Self Discipline - on-going 5S, housekeeping audits

Some healthcare organisations extend this to 6S, explicitly adding safety (Fillingham, 2007). Bicheno (2004) points out that safety should anyway be stressed in each of the five S. He also comments that while the first two are the easiest and most widely adopted, the real benefits arise from the later ones, especially standardise. An alternative is CANDO (Cleanup, Arrange, Neatness, Discipline, Ongoing improvement.

5.4.2   How the approach fits with others

Many authors writing about the Lean approach believe that *"you can integrate other approaches (particularly the tools they offer) without contradicting the core objectives of Lean – to improve customer value"* (Hines et al. 2004, Kaplan & Rona 2004), and this is demonstrated in Figure 6.

Figure 6 – Lean and its tools (Hines et al. 2004).

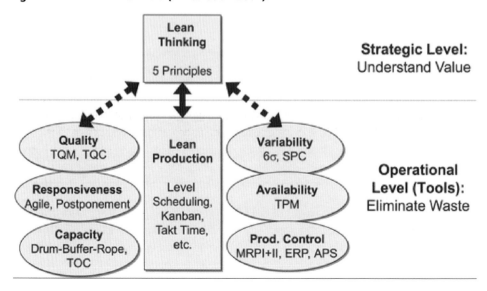

Key to Figure 6:

TQM	Total Quality Management (see section 4.3)
TQC	Total Quality Control
ToC	Theory of Constraints (see section 5.5)
6σ	Six Sigma (see section 5.3)
SPC	Statistical Process Control (see section 5.2)
TPM	Total Productive Maintenance
MRPI+II	Materials Requirements Planning
ERP	Enterprise Resource Planning
APS	Advanced Planning and Scheduling

However some argue that there are fundamental differences, based on the experimental approach used in the TPS: "The essential difference between TPS and traditional improvement programs lie in who identifies a problem and how, by whom, when, and where it is solved" (Thompson, Wolf & Spear 2003, p.587).

Lean and Six Sigma

Six Sigma and Lean are often compared because they are currently both popular with industry, especially in the US (Arnheiter & Maleyeff 2005) and have both evolved from their original routes to be comprehensive approaches to improvement. It is therefore important to compare them directly.

Six Sigma's rigorous, data-analytic search for root causes makes it well-suited for complex 'cause-unknown' problem situations. Meanwhile insights into situations where problems involve cycle-time reduction and flow improvements have often been partitioned into approaches often now labelled as Lean.

As many have tried both approaches separately, with initial success but then gradually diminishing returns, there is a move to combine the two to form Lean Six Sigma (George & Rowlands 2003). Efforts to bring Lean tools into Six Sigma, and attempt to exploit the synergy of the two (Bossert 2003), have resulted in packages with names such as Lean Six Sigma. Typically Lean tools such as value stream mapping are included in DMAIC, particularly during Measure (e.g. value stream mapping) and Improve (e.g. including established pull methods and 5S) (George, Rowlands, Price et al. 2005)).

If the two approaches are combined at a strategic level, rather than simply incorporating tools, then a Lean Six Sigma organisation would include (from Lean principles) (George 2003):

- an overriding philosophy that seeks to maximise the value-added content of all operations
- constant evaluation of incentive systems to ensure they result in global rather than local optimisation
- a management decision-making process that bases every decision on its relative impact on the customer

It would also include (from Six Sigma principles):

- a stress on data-driven methodologies in all decision-making
- methodologies that seek to minimise variation of quality
- a company-wide, highly structured, education and training programme

These proposals stem from the fact that (George 2003) Lean needs Six Sigma because:

- lean does not explicitly prescribe the culture and infrastructure needed to achieve and sustain results
- customer needs are not at the centre
- lean does not recognise the impact of variation
- it misses out the define and measure aspects of a DMAIC process

Six Sigma needs Lean because:

- it identifies waste
- it improves process speed/cycle time
- it includes methods for rapid action (kaizen)
- six Sigma quality is approached faster if Lean eliminates non value-added steps

The differences between the two approaches are also summarised by (Nave 2002) who argues that it is the organisational culture that makes the difference about which method is appropriate and that many methods appear similar when their secondary effects are considered.

Table 11 – Six Sigma and Lean

Program	Six Sigma	Lean
Theory	Reduce variation	Reduce waste
Application guidelines	Define Measure Analyse Improve Control	Identify value Identify value stream Flow Pull Perfection
Focus	Problem	Flow
Assumptions	A problem exists Figures and numbers are valued System output improves if variation in all processes is reduced	Waste removal will improve performance Many small improvements are better than systems analysis
Primary effect	Uniform process output	Reduced flow time
Secondary effects	Less waster Fast throughput Less inventory Fluctuation – performance measures for managers Improved quality	Less variation Uniform output Less inventory New accounting system Flow - performance measures for managers Improved quality
Criticisms	System interaction not considered Processes improved independently	Statistical or system analysis not valued

Other approaches to using Lean and Six Sigma include parallel roadmaps, an approach proposed by the NHS (see Figure 7).

Figure 7 – Lean Six Sigma (NHS Institute for Innovation and Improvement 2006)

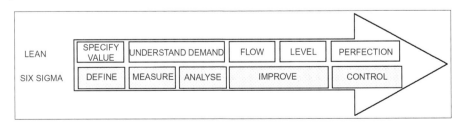

Some have also proposed new hybrid roadmaps (Rath & Strong Management Consultants 2005), or recommend applying Lean first to redesign or stabilise a process, then Six Sigma to improve it (see section 5.3.4).

5.4.3 Where the approach has been used in healthcare

The principles on which a Lean approach is based can be viewed as generic (Jones & Mitchell 2006) and therefore potentially applicable outside of manufacturing – to other service organisations and to healthcare. *"Lean thinking is … a management strategy that is applicable to all organisations because it is to do with improving processes"* (Miller 2005) p.2.

Particular features of Lean which may indicate that it is applicable to healthcare include:

- it has an overall philosophy and a way of setting priorities
- it builds on improvement that has already been carried out e.g. clearing bottlenecks in the patient journey, identifying the causes of variation, by adding "some more tolls and providing more of a framework" (Jones & Mitchell 2006 p.3). It can be argued that "There are still considerable gains to be made in terms of efficiency and effective use of resources to be achieved in public services" (Radnor & Boaden 2008) p.6
- it has a body of evidence-based tools and approaches already tested within the public sector (Radnor & Boaden 2008)
- there is a community of those trying Lean to support implementation

In addition there are features of healthcare which may make it amenable to Lean (Table 12).

Table 12 – Characteristics of healthcare that might imply that Lean is applicable

Characteristics of healthcare that make it amenable to Lean (Jones & Mitchell 2006):	How Lean can help	A Lean culture (Miller 2005)	Change in mindset that leaders need to achieve (Westwood & Silvester 2007)
things are hard to see e.g. relating to errors	Defining the problem (cf the diagnosis) is the first step (Thompson et al. 2003)	Share information	Understand demand and plan based on this
responsibilities are not clear – often made worse by patients being in various places and lack of communication between staff caring for the patient		Interdisciplinary teams	Team organised by flow – based on value stream
unnecessary work keeps being created	Its principles and tools enable the various forms of waste to be identified and their root causes tackled (Jones & Mitchell 2006)		Reduce waste

Table 12 – Characteristics of healthcare that might imply that Lean is applicable - continued...

Characteristics of healthcare that make it amenable to Lean (Jones & Mitchell 2006):	How Lean can help	A Lean culture (Miller 2005)	Change in mindset that leaders need to achieve (Westwood & Silvester 2007)
processes are not joined up – especially common where there are various departments involved in a process	It emphasises the whole system (Jones & Mitchell 2006)	Process driven	Systems thinking
inappropriate measures and targets – accounting measures in particular focus only on a single element	It highlights that *"many traditional approaches to efficiency improvement are futile and focus on the wrong thing"* (Jones & Mitchell 2006 p.2)		Managers focus on delivering value to the patients
problems are not resolved – because the root cause is not identified	*"How work is expected to proceed is specified before it is performed. This applies to delegation of responsibility (who will do what task for whom), coordination of delegated tasks and execution of delegated tasks. Work is designed so that when it proceeds contrary to expectations, this becomes immediately evident"* (Thompson et al. 2003 p. 587). Therefore, when someone experiences a problem they should not seek a 'work around' but identify the problem and call for assistance in developing a counter measure that removes the root cause that created the problem	Root cause analysis	
things get compounded because of the large number of steps in the process	It distinguishes between waste and value by not viewing all costs as the same – some costs do deliver value	Removing waste lowers cost	No delays are experienced Minimise cost of capacity
frustration dissipates energy – staff may want to do a good job but the system doesn't let them	Its focus on the things that *"matter to patients and clinicians, and on the things that cause them stress and get in the way of care"* (Jones & Mitchell 2006 p.2)		The problems generating the waste are understood, so exiting resources are more productive

Adapting Lean thinking for services

A vociferous critic of the way Lean has been applied to services is John Seddon (Seddon 2005a) who argues:

- the focus of Lean on standardisation of processes is inappropriate in services, where the time taken to perform a task can vary and standardisation may cause costs to rise, because the system cannot absorb variety, and morale may fall
- value stream mapping is of little value as it does not take account of flows being dictated by external factors i.e. the customer. It also is not primarily focused on levels of inventory but on information fit for purpose being supplied by preceding steps in the process.

Recent research has also shown that the Lean approach may need to be adapted for public services, with evidence suggesting that public services should first engage with the principles of customer and process view, flow, and reduction of waste through the use of simple tools rather than embarking on the implementation of more complex tools used in manufacturing (for example line balancing). The authors argue that *"the issues and context of the public sector means that the approach could only ever be piecemeal due to the need of service processes being able to cope with variety, uncertainty and so not being over-standardized and inflexible."* (Radnor & Boaden 2008, p.5).

Recent research has shown that there is *"relatively little evidence of the complete Lean philosophy being applied in the public sector"* (Radnor et al. 2006). There is also evidence to suggest that it is applied within the public sector without a full understanding of the underlying principles, so it is seen as another policy or set of tools, which leads to Lean being applied to processes that are not suited to it, and considered as a set of tools rather than a fundamental shift in culture and approach (Radnor & Boaden 2008).

Current guidance on implementing Lean in healthcare

Within the UK there is a developing body of guidance, being led primarily by both the NHS Institute for Innovation and Improvement and the Lean Institute. Within the US, the Lean Institute is also a major provider of training, and the Institute for Health Improvement (IHI) has also produced guidance. The main sources of information are shown in Table 13.

Table 13 – Guidance on Lean in healthcare

Institution	Key documents	Information available at
NHS Institute for Innovation and Improvement	Going Lean in the NHS (Westwood, James-Moore & Cooke 2007)	http://www.institute.nhs.uk/quality_and_value/Lean_thinking/Lean_thinking.html/
UK Lean Enterprise Academy	Presentations from the 4 UK Lean Healthcare Forums	http://www.Leanuk.org/pages/Lean_healthcare.htm
Institute for Health Improvement	Going Lean in Health Care (Miller 2005)	http://www.ihi.org
Lean Enterprise Institute	Range of articles and training programmes	http://www.Lean.org/

Although the IHI site does have cross-links to academic papers, the others in general do not (unless they are papers written by staff from those organisations). The source of information for the guidance produced – which is extensive and prescriptive – is therefore often unclear; in particular the extent to which it is based on existing evidence. Reference to key texts about Lean and the TPS (Womack & Jones 1996) does not of itself constitute an evidence-based approach since these books are themselves accounts of activity rather than research-based analyses.

How to implement Lean in healthcare

Many publications now suggest a series of steps that should be followed in order for organisations to become Lean; examples (Table 14) are all based around the five Lean principles (Womack & Jones 1996).

Table 14 – Implementing Lean

Original Lean principles (Womack & Jones 1996)	NHS Institute/University of Warwick guidance for Lean (Westwood et al. 2007)	NHS Confederation (Lean Institute) Lean guidance (Jones & Mitchell 2006)
The identification of customer value	Specify value – this can only be defined by the customer. Value is any activity which improves the patient's health, well-being and experience	Identify value streams
The management of the value stream	Identify the value stream or patient journey – the core set of actions required to deliver value for patients	Map value streams – which usually shows immediate waste
Developing the capability to flow production	Make the process and value flow – align healthcare processes to facilitate the smooth flow of patients and information	Identify and implement immediate medium-term and long-term improvements. RIEs may be used initially which will show and enable immediate improvements, but there has to be responsibility for also making the medium and longer-term improvements that will also be identified
The use of pull mechanisms to support material flow	Let the customer pull – the customer should pull products and services as needed. We should deliver care on demand, with the resources needed for it	
The pursuit of perfection through reducing all forms of waste in the system	Pursue perfection – develop and amend processes continually in pursuit of the ideal	

However, many authors also urge caution in the implementation of Lean in healthcare for a variety of reasons:

Integration with organisation strategy and structure

- lean has to be locally led and part of the organisation's strategy: it cannot be imposed from outside (Jones & Mitchell 2006)

- a strategic approach to improvement, as well as supportive organisational culture and ownership are some of the factors described as related to successful Lean implementation in the public sector (Radnor et al. 2006)

- activities must be organised by flow of patients and information rather than by functional departments. Accounting structures and reports also need to be organised in this way (Westwood & Silvester 2007)

- leaders must *"create a clear vision statement that guides people to make the right choices ... evaluate the organisational structure and work to flatten it, eliminating hierarchical layers and organising staff into operational teams based on products and services"* (Miller 2005, p.5)

Leadership and management

- executive support is essential for success – leaders must *"create the environment where applying Lean thinking can deliver results"* (Westwood et al. 2007, p.20). This will then enable frontline staff to implement the solutions to the problems they have identified

- to realise the full potential executives will *"need to do more than provide support for pilot projects ... they will need to embrace and embody TPS in their own work"* (Spear 2005, p.91)

- management commitment and capability is one of the factors described as related to successful Lean implementation in the public sector (Radnor et al. 2006). However, for Lean to work staff need to support and cooperate; it cannot be imposed by managers

Time taken to achieve benefits

- Lean is not a quick-fix and although there may be immediate improvements, the principles take time to embed. Because its application relies on the *"positive commitment and support of staff in their day-to-day work"* linking it to short-term cost-cutting measures will not lead to long-term success in its application (Jones & Mitchell 2006)

- however there may be short-term gains too: small changes make a big difference – staff often *"merely need permission to improve"* (Westwood et al. 2007, p.19)

- timing to set realistic timescales for change and to make effective use of commitments and enthusiasm for change are some of the factors described as related to successful Lean implementation in the public sector (Radnor et al. 2006)

Support and education needed

- there is debate about the extent to which external or expert support is required to implement Lean. However, some do propose a dedicated team to support the process (Thompson et al. 2003) and recommend active administrative support. Others say that dedicated improvement expertise is essential (Westwood & Silvester 2007)

- external support from consultants in the first instance, as well as provision of adequate resources to support change are some of the factors described as related to successful

Lean implementation in the public sector (Radnor et al. 2006). The same authors cite poor selection of improvement team members as a barrier to change

- some initial education is needed for all (Thompson et al. 2003)

Involvement and communication

- all levels and types of staff need to be involved: *"You need to create a shared, joint view of what is going on … in hospitals doctors find it hard to listen to anyone else"* (Jones & Mitchell 2006, p.21)
- effective communication and engagement through the organisation, as well as teamwork and joined-up whole systems thinking are some of the factors described as related to successful Lean implementation in the public sector (Radnor et al. 2006)

5.4.4   Outcomes that have been reported

In manufacturing, there is a considerable body of research (Oliver, Delbridge, Jones et al. 1994) exploring the impact of what were termed 'world class manufacturing' approaches, of which Lean is considered to be one. However, one of the few reviews of its effects focuses on just-in-time (JIT) (White, Pearson & Wilson 1999).

Where studies have considered the impact of Lean they have focused on a single aspect of Lean and its performance implications (Hackman & Wageman 1995, Samson & Terziovski 1999), or the implementation and performance relationship with two aspects of Lean (Flynn, Sakakibara & Schroeder 1995, McKone, Schroeder & Cua 2001).

Many of the findings support the general assertion that there is *"unambiguous evidence that the synergistic effects of all Lean practices are associated with better manufacturing performance. The implication for managers of plants that are not implementing Lean practices is also fairly clear. To not implement Lean bundles is likely to put plants at a performance disadvantage compared to plants that do implement, regardless of size, age or level of unionization of the plant in question"* (White et al. 1999).

Methodologically these studies are both comparative and quantitative, which may lead to less emphasis on the 'softer' benefits but would generally be regarded as more rigorous than single case studies.

Theoretically, benefits from Lean may be in 'waves' (Jones & Mitchell 2006):

- improved quality and safety – fewer mistakes
- improved delivery – better work gets done sooner
- improved throughput – same people and equipment capable of achieving more
- accelerating momentum – stable working environment with clear standardised procedures
- staff morale improves.

Places where Lean implementation in healthcare and its benefits have been reported in reports or papers include (Table 15) but the authors recognise that due to the current popularity of Lean in healthcare, such reports are being published at an increasing rate.

Table 15 – Reported outcomes from the application of Lean

Place	Source of information	Area of application	Reported benefits (examples)
UK			
Bolton Hospitals NHS Trust Has own website with information and links to other Lean sites [7]	Jones & Mitchell 2006	Pathology department	• steps in blood sample process reduced from 309 to 57 • distance walked by staff reduced by 80% • time taken to process endocrinology and haematinics samples cut from 24-30 hrs to 2-3 hrs • same amount of work done with fewer staff • space needed by department reduced by 50%
	Westwood et al. 2007	Non-elective trauma patient pathway	• 50% reduction in hospital mortality for older patients with fractured neck of femur • 37% reduction in overall mortality for adult trauma patients • 32% shorter length of stay
	Fillingham 2007	Bolton Improving Care System	• 42% reduction in paperwork associated with trauma cases • 38% decrease in time taken to get patients with fractured hip to theatre
Hereford Hospital	Westwood & Silvester 2007	Pathology turnaround times	• productivity improved by 252% • £365K annual savings through earlier patient discharge • delays in specimen reception reduced from 13 mins to 1 min
Mayday Healthcare NHS Trust	Westwood et al. 2007	Sterile services (RIE)	• flow improved, giving more consistent turnaround time • less time lost preparing theatre lists • demand smoothed throughout the day

7.   http://www.boltonhospitals.nhs.uk/publications/bics/default.htm

Table 15 – Reported outcomes from the application of Lean - continued...

Place	Source of information	Area of application	Reported benefits (examples)
Medway Trust	Mathieson 2006	Audiology	• reduced time taken to issue hearing aids from 2 years to 101 days by allowing direct GP referral to audiologists
Wirral Hospital	Mathieson 2006; Jones & Mitchell 2006	Day surgery	• doubled day surgery capacity at elective surgery site
US			
Thedacare, Wisconsin	Miller 2005	Various. Details of approach are in paper	• 3.3m$ savings in 2004 • reduced accounts receivable from 56 to 44 days in 2204, equating to about 12m$ in cash flow.
Western Pennsylvania Hospital, Pittsburgh	Spear 2005	Pre-surgery unit	• reliability of work improved: 54 problems identified and worked around e.g. time between patient signing in and registering reduced from 2hrs to 0, unnecessary blood bank reports reduced from 7 to 0 per day
Hospitals in the Pittsburgh Regional Healthcare Initiative: Lifecare Hospitals Monongahela Valley Hospital UPMS Health System Allegheny General Hospital	Spear 2005	Central line-associated bloodstream (CLAB) infections	• 87% reduction in CLAB infections, down to 0 in some places
University of Pittsburgh Medical Center (UPMC) Health System	Thompson et al. 2003	Use of IV push method	• preparation time for antibiotics reduced by 4 mins per dose, nurse savings of over 5000 hrs per year, patient does not experience discomfort before dose is changed

Table 15 – Reported outcomes from the application of Lean - continued...

Place	Source of information	Area of application	Reported benefits (examples)
Virginia Mason Medical Centre, Seattle	Reinertsen 2006	Various areas	• no of patients contracting pneumonia while on ventilator reduced from 40 to 2 per year, and costs dropped from 1.6$m to 0.1$m
	Miller 2005	Various. Details of their approach given in this paper	• inventory down 53% • floor space down 41% • distance travelled by people down 44% • setup time down 82%
	Bush 2007	Various. Examples given from each of Ohno's seven wastes (Ohno & (translator) Rosen 1995)	• waiting time from breast cancer diagnosis to initiation of treatment down from 21 to 11 days
	Nelson-Peterson & Leppa 2007	Various but focuses on nursing and includes details of how the approach is applied.	• staff walking distance down from 240 to 126 min per workflow cycle • % of nurse time spent in non value-adding activity down from 68% to 10%
Progressive Healthcare	Bushell, Mobley & Shelest 2002	Primary care delivery processes	• none reported in this paper – about process only
Intermountain Healthcare	Jimmerson et al. 2005	Various	• new medication orders lead time reduced from 4 hrs to 12 mins
Park Nicollet Health Services (PNHS), Minneapolis	Kim, Spahlinger, Kin et al. 2006	Patient access	• number of MRI and CT scans performed each day increased • urgent care wait clinical reduced from 122 to 52 minutes
Community Medical Center, Montana	Kim et al. 2006	Pathology	• report turnaround time reduced from 5 to 2 days

Table 15 – Reported outcomes from the application of Lean - continued...

Place	Source of information	Area of application	Reported benefits (examples)
Australia			
Flinders Medical Centre, Adelaide, South Australia	Jones & Mitchell 2006, Ben-Tovim, Bassham, Bennett et al. 2008a, Ben-Tovim, Bassham, Bolch et al. 2007	Redesigning Care Program: emergency department flows, medical flows, surgical flows, now also extended to support services, mental health and transition to community care	• rates of serious adverse events reported to insurers halved since programme began • average emergency waiting time fell by 25% • increase in capacity led to full functioning of elective surgery programme • costs now below budget
	Jones & Mitchell 2006	Ward 'pull' programme	• 20% increase in patient turnover, median length of stay in general medical service by one day

There are case studies of North American organisations available from a variety of sources, the main one being the web site of the Lean Enterprise Institute[8] (the US version of the UK Lean Enterprise Academy which runs the Lean Healthcare Forums). Cases include the Mayo Clinic, HôtelDieu Grace Hospital in Windsor, Ontario, and Massachusetts General Hospital.

NHS organisations reported as undertaking Lean initiatives[9] not covered above include (Table 16):

Table 16 – Reported applications of Lean in the NHS

Organisation	Area of application
Gwent NHS Trust	Various within overall improvement framework
Wirral NHS Trust	Cardiology RIE
Salisbury NHS Trust	Radiology
Wirral NHS Trust	Pre-operative assessment/elective surgery
Mayday Hospital NHS Trust	Sterile services
Kings College Hospital	Various within overall improvement framework
George Eliot Hospital NHS Trust	Diabetes
East Devon PCT	Failure demand for emergency care

In addition, a number or organisations are undertaking The Productive Ward/Community Hospital/Leader/Operating Theatre initiatives within the NHS[10] although the impact of these has yet to be formally evaluated.

8.   www.lean.org
9.   www.leanhealthcare.org.uk - Presentations from the 4 Lean Healthcare Forums that have happened to date
10.   www.institute.nhs.uk

Lean Six Sigma

It is claimed that Lean Six Sigma *"holds great promise for optimizing the delivery of health
services because it maximises stakeholder value by achieving the fastest rate of improvement
in customer satisfaction, quality, cost, process speed and invested capital"* (Forthman,
Wooster, Hill et al. 2003).

Lean Six Sigma in healthcare has been investigated in the context of its application in clinical
trials, in order to better understand customer requirements (Marti 2005) and in the context
of reducing medication errors (Esimai 2005). It is also included in a review of service
applications of Lean Six Sigma (George 2003). Outside the US, it has been applied in the
same Dutch hospital at which extensive Six Sigma use was previously noted (de Koning et
al. 2006).

Lean Six Sigma in the NHS

Following the NHS Green Belt programme (section 5.3.3), the Juran Institute also delivered
a three-day Lean Six Sigma course, based on their own suggestion for how to combine Six
Sigma and Lean *"to integrate the power of Six Sigma tools and Lean tools which can be
applied within an organisation to create the fastest rate of improvement, maximise
shareholder value and increase customer delight"* (Juran Institute 2005). The NHS Institute
then compiled a document on its view of the potential for Lean Six Sigma (NHS Institute
for Innovation and Improvement 2006) and NHS change agents continue to advocate that
the NHS should create its own version of Lean Six Sigma (Westwood & Silvester 2007).
However, there seems to be no evidence of significant use of this approach in the English
NHS, beyond a brief report of work at Hereford Hospital (Westwood & Silvester 2007)
which identifies the use of some measurement techniques (e.g. to quantify variation in
demand) and analysis techniques (to understand root causes).

5.5 Theory of Constraints

5.5.1 Outline of the approach

Theory of Constraints (ToC) developed from the Optimised Production Technology (OPT) system first proposed by Goldratt in the early 1980s (Goldratt & Cox 1984). Goldratt believed that ToC represented *"an overall theory for running an organisation"* (Goldratt 1988) and although it had evolved from factory-floor concepts, it was applicable to the whole organisation; constraints might be managerial-policy related rather than related to physical things. The basic concepts of ToC are:

- every system has at least one constraint. If this were not so *"a real system such as a profit-making organisation would make unlimited profit"* (Rahman 1998). A constraint is anything that limits the system from achieving higher performance
- the existence of constraints represents opportunities for improvement. Constraints are not viewed as negative, but as opportunities to improve

There are three components to ToC:

a. **Prerequisites:**

1. establish the goal of the organisation
2. establish what performance measurement system will support achievement of the goal

b. **The Thinking Processes (TPs)**

A set of tools, basically cause-effect diagrams, that help managers to think through answers to three generic questions that arise when identifying constraints:

1. decide what to change
2. decide what to change to
3. decide how to cause the change

This can be characterised as a generic approach to *"address policy constraints and create breakthrough situations for them using common sense, intuitive knowledge and logic"* (Rahman 1998).

Tools include the Current and Future Reality Trees

c. **The working principles, the Five Focusing Steps:**

1. Identify the system's constraints - physical, managerial or policy.
2. Decide how to exploit the system's constraints - if physical; make it as effective as possible. If managerial, eliminate it and replace with a policy that will support increased throughput.
3. Subordinate everything to the above decision - every other part of the system should be adjusted to support the maximum effectiveness of the constraint.

4. Elevate the system's constraints - if existing constraints are still the most critical, improve them until the system encounters a new constraint.

5. If in any of the previous steps a constraint is broken, go back to step 1. Do not let inertia become the next constraint - this shows that it is a continual process, and that no solution is appropriate for all time, since the system itself is dynamic.

The best-publicised result of this approach is the drum-buffer-rope (DBR) approach to managing constraints in process flow (see box). Time or stock buffers protect the constraint from starvation, with visual buffer management using a traffic-light system.

Drum-Buffer-Rope

- As the throughput-rate limiting step, the rate of work of the constraint should set the rate for the whole process – it provides the 'drumbeat'.

- Lost throughput opportunity at the constraint is capacity irretrievably lost to the whole system, so the constraint is protected from starvation by a buffer. This can be a resource buffer (containing physical items) or, in the project management (critical chain) implementation of ToC, a time buffer. The state of this protective buffer must be monitored very closely; often a traffic-light buffer-status system is used.

- To prevent unnecessary build up of inventory upstream of the constraint, work is only admitted to the process upon receipt of a pull signal from the buffer – conceptually the buffer status pulls a rope connected to the entry point to the system.

Goldratt's application of the ToC philosophy to project management has produced the Critical Chain approach (Goldratt 1997, Rand 2000) in which time buffers are used to protect the constraint of the completion date. A variation on the ToC approach is *The Decalogue* (Lepore & Cohen 1999) which uses SPC control charts as a 'front end' to find and diagnose problems to then address with ToC and stresses the links between ToC and Deming's thinking.

5.5.2   How the approach fits with others

To a greater extent than in any of the other philosophies, ToC tends to be regarded as an exclusive approach, being principally the creation of a one person, Goldratt, with training and qualifications centrally-controlled.

5.5.3   Where the approach has been used in healthcare

There are relatively few published papers on the application of the approach, despite a large number of theoretical papers. This may be because it has not been applied to any great extent, or because the applications hove not been reported.

Where it has been reported, the research is *"anecdotal and fragmented"* (Lubitsh, Doyle and Valentine 2005) and mainly from the US. Certainly this indicates a lack of substantial academic research into its application, which it is expected would have yielded papers, had it taken place. There are even fewer examples of its application in the service sector.

- Three descriptive articles of applying ToC in healthcare settings were located, one of which is also military (Breen, Burton-Houle & Aron 2002, Kershaw 2000, Womack & Flowers 1999).
- The Thinking Processes have also been used to argue that faster and sustained progress in patient safety systems will only be achieved when sufficient attention is given to root causes (Pauker, Zane & Salem 2005).

ToC in the NHS

In the UK there are two approaches to using TOC ideas in the NHS: using the Thinking Processes and the Five Focusing Steps (see section 5.5.1) routinely in tactical and operational management; and implementing constraint management software tools.

1. The concept-driven approach has been used in a limited number of hospital trusts and health boards in England, Scotland and Northern Ireland, one of which has also been using the Decalogue variant. Real application to the NHS, including cross-organisational work in mental health has been described (Ritson & O'Neill 2006, Ritson & Waterfield 2005).

- Applications in surgery have been tested as part of two doctoral theses (Lubitsh et al 2005) and (Nuttall 2005).
- Nottingham Trent University has started an MSc for NHS employees teaching a ToC approach to operations management.
- *We All Fall Down* (Wright & King 2006) is a 'business novel' in the style of *The Goal*, which gives illustrations of the application of the ToC approach (including the Thinking Processes) to improving patient flow management in the NHS.

2. The software-driven approach developed from work by Ashridge Consulting (Knight 2000/1). The key people involved from Ashridge Consulting (now working as Goldratt Consulting or QFI Consulting) decided that the most promising approach was to incorporate the drum-buffer-rope ideas in software tools at critical constraint points in patient flows, and it is this approach which now dominates UK ToC application.

- Simple time-buffer coordination and management ideas have been used to develop a set of IT tools ('Jonahs'), initially in Oxfordshire (Goldratt Group and Oxford Radcliffe Hospitals NHS Trust 2003). These help manage individual patients through database-driven traffic-light buffer management. The main three Jonahs are:
    a. monitor waiting times against the 4-hour A&E target
    b. schedule discharge arrangements to hit predicted discharge dates
    c. schedule key resources to protect operating theatre utilisation

- recording and audit of reasons for breaches of the buffers is encouraged, and can provide powerful quantitative data to support cases for more resource to protect key constraints. They are very much practical, operational reactions to current problems, rather than promoting fundamental rethinking

- the Accident and Emergency department (A&E) wait and discharge planning Jonahs have been adopted by many hospitals in England and a few in Scotland and Wales through QFI Consulting

- the discharge tool has been compared with other hospital-flow software tools (Proudlove & Boaden 2006a)

ToC is not an approach that has even been promoted on a national basis within the NHS, beyond the inclusion of The Goal on reading lists associated with various improvement training programmes. There are a number of reasons for this:

- ToC is quite complex when all the parts are considered:

- ToC is closely associated with one commercial umbrella organisation, the Goldratt Group, so there are potential issues about provision of and capacity for training and consulting. In the NHS, ToC/Goldratt is becoming identified with the software and associated implementation consulting. We have been unable to identify anyone who led improvement at a national level within the NHS who is formally trained in ToC, unlike Lean, Six Sigma etc

- there appears to a perception of arrogance about the way it is promoted as the only solution

5.5.4   Outcomes that have been reported

A review of ToC across all sectors (Mabin & Balderstone 2003) states that over 400 articles and 45 books have been published on the subject since 1993, but without much systematic assessment of its impact. This review showed that those manufacturing organisations employing ToC did report it to be a substantial source of competitive advantage, but that many did not use the thinking process aspects of ToC.

The lack of rigour in reported research means that there is little evidence that has been independently assessed.

- analysis of the use of drum-buffer-rope management (Lubitsh et al. 2005) found some, though not dramatic, improvement in two of three surgical specialties and noted the impact of organisational complexity and culture, and the importance of tailoring implementation to local circumstances

- similarly, (Nuttall 2005) achieved modest improvements in performance and noted fundamental cultural barriers in the organisation such as the absence of consensus on the 'goal' of the organisation and externally and internally imposed performance measures

- the Thinking Processes are claimed to have fitted well with NHS culture and facilitated negotiation between professionals (Ritson & O'Neill 2006, Ritson & Waterfield 2005)

- the Ashridge work (Knight 2000/1) claims a variety of outcomes, summarised as the ability to *"simultaneously increase the number of patients treated and improve the quality of care and without extra resources"* (Knight 2000/1)

- subsequently (Umble & Umble 2006) reproduced Goldratt Consulting/QFI data that illustrates considerable improvement in A&E four-hour performance in the period following A&E Jonah implementation. No formal evidence of the effects of using the other Jonah tools has been published, beyond anecdotes and internal results presented at conferences

---

QUESTIONS TO THINK ABOUT:

What is the goal of your organisation?
What are your system's constraints - physical, behavioural or policy?
How might the principles of ToC be used?
What is the 'drum' driving the pace of flow in your processes?

5.6 Mass Customisation

5.6.1 Outline of what the approach is

Mass customisation is generally defined as *"the ability to produce products or services in high volume, yet vary their specification to the needs of individual customers or type of customer"* (Slack, Chambers & Johnston 2007, p.47). It is intrinsically linked to the variability of the process and the resultant service provided (see section 6.1.5).

Customising each product or service for each customer can mean high costs, and has been described a *"both an imperative and a potential curse"* (Gilmore & Pine II 1997, p.91). Warnings that *"any operations wishing to push their processes in this direction need to think very carefully about the technology and skills required to operate effectively, and profitably, in this area."* (Johnston & Clark 2005, p.191) abound, yet interest in this approach continues to increase. One way of addressing the cost and complexity challenges may be to be clear about the type of customisation to be pursued (Gilmore & Pine II 1997):

- collaborative: dialogue with individual customers to help them identify their needs and then to produce customised products or services for them

- adaptive: a standardised product is offered, that can be customised

- cosmetic: presenting a standard product differently to different customers, usually through packaging

- transparent: providing customers with unique goods and services without letting them know that they have been customised for them. Appropriate when customer needs are predictable or can be easily deduced

These approaches can be combined but may have implications for the way in which the organisation operates. It has also been suggested that various principles of operation may apply to any type of customisation, again to minimise cost and complexity:

- *Develop standard modules.* 'Menus' of standard services can be developed, which can then be arranged in appropriate combinations to provide a degree of customisation for individual customers. The achievement of customisation is therefore contingent on the management of the combination of services rather than the development of new services. (Johnston & Clark 2005)

- *Postpone customisation until the latest possible stage.* In this approach the delivery process is standardised for all stages until the last possible moment. This allows the service to gain the benefits of efficiency and consistency that are found in high volume/low variety processes (McLaughlin & Kaluzny 2000, p.77)

- *Understand the process by which customisation takes place* (McLaughlin 1996).

In pursuing mass customisation, when the number of service delivery processes increases significantly, a major transition can occur. In such circumstances it is recommended:

- flexibility of the parts of the organisation dealing directly with customers is increased

- customer-facing staff are required to give informed advice as to the best service for an individual customer

- customer-facing staff are 'upskilled' through a combination of greater staff training and supportive information systems

- processes are designed to be more flexible and allow greater discretion on the part of the employee (Johnston & Clark 2005)

However, an alternative view of mass customisation (Boynton, Victor & Pine 1993) describes it as a strategy to be adopted by organisations where process change is stable but product/service change is dynamic. Other strategy options in this model are mass production (for stable process and product change), innovation (where both process and product change is dynamic) and continuous improvement (where process change is dynamic but product/service change is stable).

A theoretical assessment of the application of this model within healthcare (McLaughlin & Kaluzny 2000) highlights that the path to mass customisation as a strategy is different in healthcare from other industries. Healthcare is traditionally a 'craft' industry, characterised by process innovation and product variety. Following a move to more emphasis on process improvement, healthcare may then develop into mass production, but only if *"the approach is sufficiently cut and dried, the volume is high and the patient will accept this impersonal mode of delivery"* (McLaughlin & Kaluzny 2000, p.77). These authors then see mass customisation as the strategy *"that will satisfy health care customers at low or reasonable relative costs"* (McLaughlin & Kaluzny 2000, p.77), although it will involve less stability in healthcare processes as effectiveness improves (McLaughlin 1996).

5.6.2 How the approach fits with other approaches

This approach is different in that it is not an approach to improvement, but rather one focusing on process and system design (see section 6.1.3).

It is increasingly argued by some authors that mass customisation is the next stage after process improvement activities, which are *"simply stopping points on the way to the efficient and effective health care system that consumers desire"* (McLaughlin & Kaluzny 2000, p.82). However, there is no empirical evidence presented to support this assertion.

5.6.3 Where the approach has been used in healthcare

Despite a large number of research papers detailing mass customisation in a manufacturing environment, there is a paucity of literature that describes the application of the approach to healthcare, or even to other types of service organisation. Reasons for this may include:

- the natural process variability and the high degree of autonomy in healthcare systems (McLaughlin & Kaluzny 1997)
- the fact that a change to more customisation is required, but has not yet been; *"We should be able to coach organisations to implement … models that we will change as we learn, so as to achieve that other industries call 'mass customisation'"* (Berwick 2005, p.325)
- the technology is not readily available. The US-based Center for the Health Professions advocates the use of mass customisation in healthcare but believes that the *'high tech and high touch' (Naisbitt 2001) approach that is required 'is well beyond where health care is today'*[11]

However, some authors have described the potential of mass customisation to improve healthcare as:

- a mechanism for creating more effective health professional teams that can measure results and systematically improve clinical outcomes while reducing costs (James 2005)
- a means of maintaining system performance as processes change. NHS hospitals have been viewed as the service equivalent of a batch manufacturing system (Silvestro 1999) as patients are moved from one department to another in complex, long distance stop-start flow patterns. However, it widely recognised that processes must move from batch to mass production as their output volume increases or the performance of the system can be seriously affected (Walley et al. 2006a)
- a benefit for disease management as it permits patient subcategories that are large enough to warrant separate contact but not so small that they present an administrative burden (Miller 2003)

- a mechanism for better meeting the needs of patients. A study that examined the potential of mass customisation (Thompson & Nussbaum 2000) concluded that there are *"practice opportunities and the need for further research in order to implement mass customisation in healthcare"* (Thompson & Nussbaum 2000 p.19). The notion of improving flexibility in systems is also described as important here: *"It is the waste and inflexibility of our own work system that forces us into uniformity towards patients when more agile systems would respect their diversity"* (Berwick 1997)

Other examples of applications include:

> Custom printed information materials that are built for each individual patient and are termed *'snowflake technology'* as no two patients receive exactly the same information (Miller 2003 p.47)

> Clinical pathways that integrate information systems to provide highly specific information about each patient-background, preferences, health status and the optimal co-ordination of services (Fitzgerald & McLaughlin 2001)

> It is argued the NHS Direct telephone service follows a *"hybrid mass customisation model"* (Goode & Greatbatch 2005, p.316). As the service is purely an advice line its impact on healthcare, and the value of taking a mass customisation approach, has been difficult to ascertain (Florin & Rosen 1999).

5.6.4   Outcomes that have been reported

There are no independently evaluated examples of outcomes of mass customisation in healthcare that have been reported to date.

> **QUESTIONS TO THINK ABOUT:**
>
> Are there any processes in your organisation for which mass customisation could be appropriate?
> How will you identify the needs of your customers?

11.   http://futurehealth.ucsf.edu/from_the_director_0105.html.

6. UNDERLYING CONCEPTS

The approaches to quality improvement detailed in this report are all based on a series of underlying concepts, with different emphasis on each one depending on the approach concerned. The purpose of this section is to outline these concepts and to show how they support the various approaches to quality improvement, as well as to demonstrate the implications for using the approaches in practice. Their application to the healthcare context will also be explored.

These concepts might be described as underlying operations management, a well-established academic discipline (Voss 1995); although the concepts are described in different ways by differing authors (Slack et al. 2007).

Every organisation has a function that can be described as operations because every organisation produces products, services or a combination of the two. Operations management focuses on examining the processes that are used to produce these goods and services. Effective operations management has the potential to keep costs down, improve revenue, appropriately allocate resources and develop future competitive advantage (Slack et al. 2007). It has been argued that modern operations management principles are supportive of what many clinicians have been suggesting for a long time (Walley 2003a) but it is argued that research in healthcare rarely take an operations management perspective (Davies & Walley 2000).

The concepts described here are:

- systems and processes
    - o systems thinking in healthcare
    - o the process view
    - o process design in healthcare
    - o managing flow
    - o variation
- the role of the customer
- balancing supply and demand:
    - o capacity management
    - o demand management
    - o inventory management

In each section, the link between the concepts and the approaches to improvement (see section 5) is described, along with any evidence of the use of these concepts within healthcare.

6.1 Systems and processes

Systems thinking has been an approach to viewing organisations for many years, with the divergence between hard systems and soft systems being made later in its development (Checkland 1981). Systems thinking is also the basis of recent emphasis on organisational learning (Senge 1990). It can be described as exploration of *"the properties which exist once the parts [of the system] have been combined into a whole"* (Iles & Sutherland 2001).

This systems view is claimed by operations management academics as the key to their approach (Slack, Chambers, Johnston et al. 2006), and it described as one of the *"persistent themes"* in a recent review of the development of the operations management field (Sprague 2007)

The systems view is fundamental to a lot of the thinking in improvement, perhaps particularly to Deming's insights, and is inherent in many of the approaches discussed in section 4. This has been appreciated to be a strength in the healthcare context, e.g. *"healthcare is taught to look at the system – that's exactly what Six Sigma does"* (Scalise 2003). Other authors argue that an operations management approach based on systems can be applied to hospitals (Mango & Shapiro 2001)

A current proponent of systems thinking in the public sector and healthcare context is John Seddon, whose approach is built on interpreting and applying the fundamental principles of Deming and the TPS in the context of service organisations; a Lean approach but with few tools (Seddon 2005a). It emphasises understanding demand and the capability of the system, introducing appropriate measures, introducing 'cLean' flow, reducing failure demand and designing a system to absorb variation. Seddon has adopted the label 'systems thinking' for these principles, and claims that this is *"diametrically opposed to command and control thinking"* (Table 17).

Table 17 – Command and control versus systems thinking (Seddon 2005a)

COMMAND AND CONTROL THINKING		SYSTEMS THINKING
Top-down, hierarchy	**Perspective**	Outside-in, system
Functional	**Design**	Demand, value and flow
Separated from work	**Decision-making**	Integrated with work
Output, targets, standards: related to budget	**Measurement**	Capability, variation: related to purpose
Contractual	**Attitude to customers**	What matters?
Contractual	**Attitude to suppliers**	Cooperative
Manage people and budgets	**Role of management**	Act on the system
Control	**Ethos**	Learning
Reactive, projects	**Change**	Adaptive, integral
Extrinsic	**Motivation**	Intrinsic

A full systems view of improvement should avoid the risk of local improvement resulting in sub-optimisation of the wider system. Of the approaches discussed in section 4, TOC is most explicit in emphasising looking upwards to appreciating the overall goal of the system and using performance measurement systems that support this goal.

6.1.1 Systems thinking in healthcare

Systems thinking has also been proposed as a means of understanding medical systems (Nolan 1998), based on the following principles:

- a system needs a purpose to aid people in managing interdependencies
- the structure of a system significantly determines the performance of the system
- changes in the structure of a system have the potential for generating unintended consequences
- the structure of a system dictates the benefits that accrue to various people working in the system
- the size and scope of a system influence the potential for improvement
- the need for co-operation is a logical extension of interdependencies within systems
- systems must be managed
- improvements in systems must be led

  Design of healthcare systems has focused in more recent years on hospitals forming health service partnership based networks aimed to provide the public with access to a broad spectrum of services and seamless coordinated care (Addicott & Ferlie 2007, Li, Benton & Keong Leong 2002). Cancer services are an early example of this practice. Managed Clinical Networks (MCNs) have been established by the NHS *"as a means to streamlining patient pathways and fostering the flow of knowledge and good practice between the many different professions and organisations involved in care"* (Addicott & Ferlie 2007 p.393). The aim is that all providers of cancer care for a defined population work together to deliver high quality care (Leese, Heywood, Allgar et al. 2006). The evidence of their effectiveness to date is developing quickly (Addicott, McGivern & Ferlie 2006, Robert et al. 2003) and the transfer of knowledge between practitioners as part of network activity has been shown to be substantial (Nicolini, Powell, Conville et al. 2007).

6.1.2   The process view

A consequence of viewing organisation and networks, as systems is an increased focus on the processes which comprise such systems. Academics from many fields have recognised the importance of the process view, where process management is defined as entailing three practices: mapping processes, improving processes and adhering to systems of improved processes (Benner & Tushman 2003) – an approach that is reflected in much study of both quality improvement and patient safety.

Clinical and managerial processes have sometimes been interpreted as discrete and a largely unconnected set of activities within the delivery of healthcare (Sorensen & Ledema 2008), with the subsequent effect of producing misaligned objectives and a lack of strategic focus on the most important areas for improvement. The conflict between clinical and managerial priorities is often most apparent when defining quality, especially when performance metrics are associated with tangible aspects of process quality (e.g. waiting times) rather than patient experience or clinical outcomes.

It is argued that taking a process view is one of the key characteristics of organisations who are successful in improvement, along with adopting evidence-based practice, learning collaboratively and being ready and able to change (Plsek 1999). This process view is not only about changing organisations but also examining and improving the interaction between elements of the organisation, including the individuals who work within them.

It is interesting that the approach which has probably had the biggest impact in the NHS to date (PDSA) does not explicitly refer to processes (Langley et al. 1996), although the approach appears to be based on the assumption that work is or can be organised into processes. Given the origin of this, and many other quality improvement approaches, in the manufacturing sector it was perhaps seen to be obvious that work was organised in this way.

A key principle of operations management relates to processes and their design. This includes physical layout, but is not limited to this, as the increased emphasis on services and their organisation means that processing information is vital to the effective operation of organisations.

The Lean and TOC approaches focus on flow, so have tools in their toolkits to design flow systems according to their philosophies. Other improvement approaches focus more on the analysis of existing process design, rather than providing guidance on how to design a process.

6.1.3   Process design in healthcare

Designing care processes is cited as a key decision area within healthcare delivery systems (Roth 1993). As the outcomes of the healthcare delivery process include the patients' health status and their perceptions of their care experience, Roth (1993) suggests four factors that play a role in designing healthcare processes:

1. Explicit healthcare services: these are the service processes that satisfy the basic healthcare needs of patients.
2. Implicit benefits: these include psychological or 'implied' benefits derived from the service encounter, such as relief or delight.
3. Delivery channels: this factor includes the patient interface with the organisation and the availability of relevant information regarding this interface.

4. Facilitating materials: these are the support tools, techniques, services, supplies and goods used in providing care.

The principles of process design have been used in a variety of situations within healthcare:

*   some success in using operations management approaches in redesigning process layouts has been described (Walley et al. 2006a), albeit not known to be operations management by the hospitals involved, based on volume variation analysis in A&E departments

*   the NHS Institute for Innovation and Improvement has champion process redesign as an effective way to achieve the target of an 18-week patient pathway through its 'No Delays' programme[12]

*   experience based design (EBD) as a way of capturing and understanding how patients' and carers' experience healthcare in order to improve services[13]

*   various experiences of process redesign in Australia have been reported (MacLellan, Cregan, McCaughan et al. 2008, McGrath, Bennett, Ben-Tovim et al. 2008, O'Connell, Ben-Tovim, McCaughan et al. 2008). The stages that may be involved in a redesign programme are shown in Figure 8

Some change initiatives within healthcare have been labelled as process redesign (Locock 2003) although these have tended to be focused on single processes rather than whole organisations. There appears to be an interest in the term 'process redesign' (Ben-Tovim et al. 2008b), as shown in Figure 8, although closer examination shows that these initiatives are also labelled as Lean.

Figure 8 – The phases of clinical process redesign (Ben-Tovim et al. 2008b)

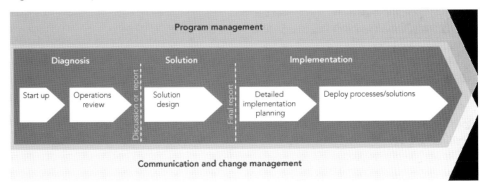

12.   http://www.institute.nhs.uk/no_delays/introduction/no_delays.html
13.   http://www.institute.nhs.uk/quality_and_value/introduction/experience_based_design.html

6.1.4 Managing flow

Flow through a process is a key concept in operations management, largely derived from the manufacturing experience. While this draws on the concepts of capacity, demand and inventory (see section 6.3), it merits separate consideration because of its current popularity in healthcare.

The Lean approach focuses on elements of processes, to operationalise its principles of smooth pull-based flow. Similarly ToC leads to the design of a process with the focus on a critical buffer which protects the key constraint to maximising the system's goal, with a rope pull mechanism.

The importance of flow is increasingly emphasised within healthcare (Brideau 2004), with work by IHI in the IMPACT network in the US (Haraden & Resar 2004). These authors maintain that understanding variation (see section 6.1.5) is essential to improving flow. The basis of the IHI approach is summarised in Table 18.

Table 18 - IHI approach to improving flow (Institute for Healthcare Improvement 2003)

Step 1: Evaluate flow: how much of the time do you get it right?
Step 2: Measure and understand flow variation
Step 3: Test changes to improve flow changes within the hospital changes that result in cooperative relationships with other healthcare providers outside the hospital

Understanding and evaluating flow requires more detailed understanding of demand and capacity than has often been the case in healthcare organisations (Horton 2004).

One author (Zimmerman 2004) proposes that studying and improving flow leads to a need to consider alignment – within the whole healthcare system, within pre-hospital care, of goals within the system, especially between healthcare organisations and clinicians. This will inevitably lead to whole-systems approaches to improvement (see section 6.1.1).

6.1.5 Variation

The emphasis on variation in the improvement approaches discussed in section 4 differs. Approaches based on statistical thinking (SPC, Six Sigma) are based on the principles that (Antony 2004):

- all work occurs in a system of interconnected processes
- variation exists in all processes
- understanding and analysing the variation are keys to success (Snee 1990).

Lean also suggests reducing process variation (in the interests of making flow as smooth as possible).

These principles are also in line with Deming's view (Deming 1986) that as variation is reduced, quality is improved. The way in which these principles may fit with an overall quality improvement approach is shown in Figure 9.

Figure 9 - Statistical Thinking in Quality Improvement (Snee 1990)

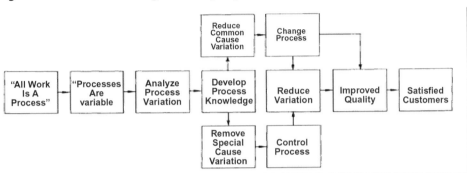

In contrast, ToC stresses the design of processes to absorb the inevitable variation in demand volume and the variability in its content through buffer management. A realisation of the importance of absorbing variation and variety, including the use of mass customisation (see section 5.6) in attempts to use Lean in UK public services has been observed (Radnor & Walley 2006).

Variation is argued to be inherent in healthcare (Haraden & Resar 2004), and the result of clinical (patient) flow, and professional variability (Institute for Healthcare Improvement 2003). Patient variability is random and cannot be eliminated or reduced, but must be managed, whereas non-random variability should be eliminated. This links with the concepts of causes of variation which are the basis of SPC (see section 5.2). It is argued (Institute for Healthcare Improvement 2003) that *"it is variation … that causes most of the flow problems in our hospital systems"*.

6.2 The role of the customer

Another concept which underpins most of the approaches in this review is that of identifying the customer, who may be internal or external to the organisation, and subsequently the needs of the customer. Whether the customer is explicitly identified, or whether their requirements are translated into a clear objective for a process (the first principle of medical systems identified by (Nolan 1998)), the purpose of the process has to be clear before improvement can take place. All industrial approaches to quality improvement involve the identification of the customer, who may be internal or external to the organisation and, subsequently, their needs.

- in Six Sigma what is 'critical to quality' as far as the customer is concerned is used to define the measures used to determine the 'defects' to be reduced
- similarly, in Lean the customer's conception of value (which might be thought of as the ratio of benefits to costs) defines which bits of processes are useful (value-adding), the rest being waste (steps or components the customer would not wish to pay for)
- interestingly, while Six Sigma and Lean are predicated on the principle that the system should seek to provide more quality or benefit to the customer and/or at lower cost, ToC does not automatically assume this is the way to maximise the goal of the organisation

6.2.1 Who is the customer in healthcare?

The concept of customer needs driving improvement was developed in manufacturing where the 'customers' of a process are usually easy to identify. Usually they are those receiving the product of the process and – critically – the ones to make the judgement on whether they wish to pay for that product at that level of quality at that cost.

However, this is more complex in healthcare systems and whether the 'customer' can be defined as the patient is open to question. This issue has been debated especially in the context of Lean implementation, where the customer is the driver of value and questions have been asked about *"the extent to which patients, service providers, or even taxpayers equate to customers in the commercial setting and the way in which health outcomes, patient satisfaction, or even cost can be legitimately used to define value."* (Young et al. 2004, p.162). Views on this include:

- the customer *"will generally be the patient"* (Jones & Mitchell 2006, p.16)

- *"An "obvious" customer in healthcare is the patient. However, other customers exist. A customer is someone who uses something that it made or was provided by a previous process step"* (Westwood et al. 2007, p.5)

- the patient may be seen as the primary customer, but the patient does not pay directly for services where they are publicly funded – other customers may include the patient's family, and society in general, as well as commissioners. *"Depending on the perspective, the definition of value will hence differ. However, because the main mission of healthcare is to treat and cure patients … it is argued that the patient should define what creates value in healthcare"* (Kollberg, Dahlgaard & Brehmer 2007, p.12)

- in the public sector the processes by which decisions are made could themselves be regarded as the customers. The principle of due process (Scorsone 2008) may determine the steps in the process and the pace at which they are carried out, whether or not they are perceived as adding value

It is clear that to date patient involvement in quality improvement has been limited (Silvester et al. 2004) with lack of attention to the presence of the patient in processes (Shortell, Levin, O'Brien et al. 1995) and lack of consumer power also being cited as important (Zbabada, Rivers & Munchus 1998). It is also argued that the market structure of healthcare in the UK at least does not enable 'consumers' to alter the behaviour of healthcare providers as there is no effective choice (Zbabada et al. 1998).

6.3 Balancing supply and demand

Balancing the supply of services with the demand for them is often referred to as planning and control and is perhaps the more traditional territory of operations management. As a result this is the area where there has perhaps been most application of operations management principles within healthcare. There are several aspects to this:

6.3.1 Capacity management

Capacity management is the ability to balance demand from customers (or patients) with the capability of the service delivery system to satisfy the demand (Armistead & Clarke 1994).

In examining the use of capacity management in four NHS trusts one study concluded that *"there appeared to be little correlation between approaches to capacity management from clinical perspectives, and those which appear in the service management literature'"* (Davies & Walley 2000, p.24). It is argued that capacity management proves difficult in hospitals due to the scheduling and processing of patients and the difficulty in consistently gaining high utilisation of resources because capacity bottlenecks move within the healthcare system (Walley et al. 2006a). There is evidence that the focus of most hospitals is on long-term aggregate capacity due to demand trends and budgetary requirements. As a result, healthcare managers do not respond to incremental changes in volume or variety, leading to a mismatch between skill mixes, staff grading and job design compared to ideal process requirements (Davies & Walley 2000).

Bed management has been described as a component of healthcare capacity management (National Audit Office 2000), with the purpose of bed management being defined in the following terms: *"hospitals have to balance, ensuring the availability of beds against the efficient utilisation of an expensive hospital resource"* management (National Audit Office 2000, p.33). However, research shows that in practice bed managers are rarely consulted about capacity planning issues (Boaden, Proudlove & Wilson 1999, Gemmel & Van Dierdonck 1999).

Like all operations, healthcare systems have to cope with varying demand and supply and will need to consider adjusting capacity accordingly. Operations management theory details various plans for treating such variation (Slack et al. 2007):

Level capacity plan

This ignores demand fluctuations and keeps nominal capacity levels constant. A level capacity strategy elevates the cost objective for hospitals seeking to maximise the utilisation of scarce resources, such as those tied to acute inpatient beds, under the premise that patients are willing to wait for services they highly value.

Chase demand plan

This adjusts capacity to reflect fluctuations in demand. A chase demand strategy recognises the pre-eminence of service quality, particularly in relation to waiting times for patient access. The initiation of 'winter plans' starting in 1996, where NHS hospitals and wider social and healthcare service capacities were increased, arguably demonstrates that chase demand strategies have been increasingly adopted as service quality has become less negotiable (Department of Health 2004).

Coping

A further capacity management strategy has been termed as 'coping' (Johnston & Clark 2005) - when operations are too busy and perceived quality begins to decline (Armistead & Clarke 1994). Hospital coping strategies noted in the literature include:

- a practice termed as outlying, where patients are placed into beds from alternate bed pools that are capable of meeting minimum medical needs. Although this practice usually involves putting an emergency medical patient (a medical outlier) into a surgical bed, the reverse is possible. Such approaches are believed to decrease productivity (National Audit Office 2000), and any subsequent repatriation transfers are anecdotally said to increase the length of stay by one day per move, thus increasing costs whilst reducing the capacity available (Proudlove, Gordon & Boaden 2003)
- re-designating beds to meet patient needs. Examples include switching male wards to female wards or vice versa. It is reported that 87% of NHS trusts use this approach (National Audit Office 2000)
- load sharing, where emergency patients are admitted in one hospital's A&E department and transferred for placement in another hospital's beds (Boaden et al. 1999)
- expediting inpatient discharges from acute beds. It is reported that 98% of acute trusts used this approach (National Audit Office 2000)
- cancellations of elective patients. This practice has been described as an important 'safety valve' for coping with bed crises wherein the needs of one customer group are traded against another (Jones, Joy & Pearson 2002)

Armistead and Clark (1994) highlight that although coping practices are in common use by a variety of frontline staff in service industries, most managers are unaware of entering coping zones and what the trigger points are. Such findings suggest that coping is a tactic rather than a strategy as its implementation is uncontrolled, unplanned and lacking objective measures to ascertain whether the operation is about to enter or leave the 'coping zone'

(Conyon 2006). For example research in healthcare has shown that:

- 25% of hospitals do not make short-term forecasts about likely bed availability (National Audit Office 2000)
- limited used is made of demand pattern data and information systems are poor (Boaden et al. 1999)
- bed managers have been described as being permanently engaged in 'firefighting' with 'no beginning and end' (Morell, Green & Armstrong 1994), indicating that coping is the norm and not a distinct strategy

6.3.2   Demand management

An alternative to managing capacity is to attempt to alter the demand for the service: demand management. Services have different characteristics from products and unused production (lost service potential) cannot be stored for sale (use) later. Research shows a limited understanding of the nature of demand in hospitals, the implications of which are delays for patients (Davies & Walley 2000).

Examples of demand management in healthcare include:

- in a study of US obstetrics (Heineke 1995) demand for hospital services was shown to depend on many unpredictable factors, such as the time that services are needed and the type of professional skill that is required. Better performance was associated with clear policies regarding access and the use of very structured procedures for patient admissions
- a survey conducted in US community hospitals found that an emphasis on demand management contributed to more desirable cost and quality performance, which lead to a better financial performance (Li et al. 2002). The use of guidelines has been advocated to manage the issues of hospital inpatient admission and inpatient and output surgical schedules based on expected length of stay

Failure demand

Demand for services can also be created as a result of not satisfying the customer the first time. This is sometimes labelled failure demand (Seddon 2005a), and can result from a number of system failures: part of the system having earlier failed to satisfactorily provide the service; a customer failing to understand the system's expectations of them or being unaware of an alternative, more-appropriate system; or the organisation not having such an alternative. This is a major waste of capacity in systems such as call centres. Failure demand has a huge impact on NHS capacity, for example A&E attendances or GP referrals leading to inappropriate emergency admissions (of patients who don't need inpatient treatment) and inadvertent admissions (of patients needing treatment of a type for which a more appropriate pathway is not available).

6.3.3 Inventory management

Inventory can be used to maintain operational performance by providing a buffer against uncertainty and variation of demand and supply (Slack et al. 2007). There is a performance trade-off associated with keeping inventories; although process utilisation is increased, inventories can adversely affect the time a job has to wait in queues and increase the storage costs. There is a view that reducing inventory will lead to the exposure of other systems issues which are otherwise hidden (see Figure 10).

Figure 10 – Reducing the level of inventory enables management to see the problems (Slack et al. 2006).

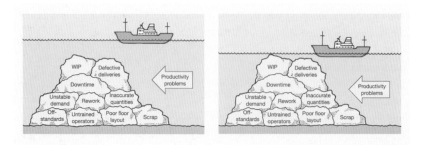

Inventory in service organisations can be interpreted as people (customers) waiting in a queue. Waiting time in the queue is a function of:

- V (the variability in the queuing system)
- U (the utilisation of the queuing system, that is, demand versus capacity)
- T (the processing times at the station).

This leads to the VUT formula (Slack, Chambers & Johnston 2004) in operations management: queuing time will increase as variability, utilisation or processing time increases.

> This was illustrated in the NHS by an analysis of the impact of bed utilisation on length of wait for admission (Bagust, Place & Posnett 1999). This influential work led to the DH recommending a bed utilisation target for hospitals. However, the differing VUT trade-off resulting from different contexts (e.g. emergency medical vs. elective surgical units) was misunderstood by some leading improvement in hospitals (Proudlove et al. 2007).

It is reported that many patient 'inventories' remain hidden, only being identified through ad hoc manually collated surveys (Audit Commission 2003, National Audit Office 2000) since they do not always constitute physical queues. Even where the patients were physically present, pressure to meet NHS A&E waiting time targets is reported to have led to patients being 'stored' as inventory (Walley et al. 2006a), unnoticed in a bed not a trolley, instead of being observed carefully by the right people and equipment.

Queuing is also about the experience of those in the queue, and in parallel with more general findings in operations management findings about the subjective experience being in a queue (Slack et al. 2004), it has been found that simple steps can improve patients queuing experiences. Efforts to keep patients informed of the likely length of wait improve perceptions of service quality (Lovelock 1992). Patients were found to be happier to queue if (Green & Armstrong 1994):

- they believed that hospital staff were aware of them
- they believed that something was happening
- they knew what to expect

Moreover, patient perceptions of what was most medically urgent also influenced their readiness to wait for admission, with cases described where patients actually believed that others should go before them in the queue (Green & Armstrong 1994).

Differences between the perceived wait of emergency patients waiting in A&E for a bed and recorded lengths of waits on hospital information systems have also been published and show that patients perceived their waits to be longer than the hospital reports indicated (Healthcare Commission 2006a). This may be attributed to:

- inaccuracies in hospital reporting systems (Conyon 2006)
- the patient experience making waiting time seem longer than it was (Lovelock 1992)
- escalating customer expectations despite reductions in customer waiting times (Healthcare Commission 2006a)

6.4 Underlying concepts and approaches to improvement

The concepts described in the previous sections are all used in the approaches to improvement, but the emphasis varies.

Table 19 summarises the key foci of each approach in relation to the concepts of process, customer focus, variation and flow.

Table 19 – The relationship of the approaches to the main concepts

	Process view	Variation	Flow	Customer focus
PDSA	All approaches assume there is a process focus, although some regard it as more fundamental than others	All these themes may be important, depending on the answer to the first question from the model for improvement and the change concepts derived as a result of considering the third question		
SPC		Main focus		Leads to definition of control limits for process
Six Sigma		Main focus		The driver for definition of what needs to be improved
Lean		Reducing waste, which may be related to variation and/or flow, is the focus. Flow tends to be emphasised more (Seddon 2005b)		Leads to the definition of value which determines where improvement is focused
ToC			Main focus	Leads to the definition of performance measures and targets for improvement

QUESTIONS TO THINK ABOUT:

Do you know who your customers are?

How do you balance the competing needs and wants of different customer groups?

What techniques do you use to balance the supply of your services with the demand for them?

What is your predominant approach to quality improvement? How do you know whether it is the most appropriate?

In what situations, and when, might it matter which approach to improvement you are using, and how rigorously you are using it?

7. TRANSLATING IMPROVEMENT APPROACHES TO THE HEALTHCARE CONTEXT

Many of the issues about translation stem from the exploration of the extent to which healthcare may be different from other industries, and the implications this may have for the application of quality improvement approaches in this sector. Other translation issues focus on the success (or otherwise) of these approaches in other sectors and how research in this area may be judged.

7.1 The difference between healthcare and other sectors

Even within the public sector, an argument can be made that the healthcare sector is different; an argument that does not simply apply to healthcare in the UK, with healthcare organisations described as showing *"striking fragmentation and turbulence that impede their capacity to provide quality care ..."* (Ramanujam & Rousseau 2006, p.811).

Compared to the private sector, the NHS can be characterised by (Pollitt 1993):

- the range and diversity of stakeholders
- tts complex ownership and resourcing arrangements
- the professional autonomy of many of its staff

Healthcare may be simply different in emphasis from other public services, rather than fundamentally different from other service organisations (Radnor & Boaden 2008).

7.1.1 Healthcare is a professional service

Like accountancy and law, healthcare organisations are 'professional' (Mintzberg 1979) and characterised by high levels of professional autonomy. Details of the implications of this are well summarised elsewhere (Buchanan, Fitzgerald & Ketley 2007) but some of the elements are shown below:

Features of the professional organisation

- Professionals have considerable autonomy and discretion, as their work involves the application of knowledge and expertise to complex problems
- Professionals are loyal to their profession and committed to their clients rather than to their employing organisation
- Professionals work independently, without reference to each other or to management
- Managers cannot develop strategy independently, but must persuade professionals to support and champion initiatives
- High-quality work is based on internalised values, beliefs and aspirations, developed through training, rather than on formal bureaucratic controls

(Buchanan et al. 2007, p.253), based on (Brock, Powell & Hinings 1999)

Other authors refer to the craft nature of clinical work and how this differs from a focus on systems: *"the hospital doctor acting as a skilled craftsperson … managing their own waiting list of patients, clinics and operations inside some else's mass production general hospital"* (Jones 2006), although some would view this now as an outdated model.

The dominance of the medical profession is especially seen when quality improvement is considered – *"quality has become a battleground on which professions compete for ownership and definition of quality"* (Øvretveit 1997). It is also argued that for health professionals, translation starts from their own world and although the change concepts (see section 5.1) may be the same for different clinical areas, success in translation only comes from promotion by other peers in the same field. Differences of span of managerial control and the relative dominance of rational decision-making processes were also cited as key issues (Arndt & Bigelow 1995). Some of these issues are summarised as clinician lack of perception of the applicability of quality improvement, and the fact that many improvement initiatives in the NHS have been led by managers, often excluding clinicians (Silvester et al. 2004).

The professional culture and the way in which it may compare with the type of organisational culture generally considered appropriate for quality improvement is described by a number of authors (Short & Rahmin 1995). Table 20 refers to TQM specifically, although the principles are common to most quality improvement initiatives.

Table 20 – Comparison of hospital professional and TQM models (Short & Rahmin 1995)

PROFESSIONAL	TQM
Individual responsibilities	Collective responsibilities
Professional leadership	Managerial leadership
Autonomy	Accountability
Administrative authority	Participation
Goal expectations	Performance and process expectations
Rigid planning	Flexible planning
Responses to complaints	Benchmarking
Retrospective performance appraisal	Concurrent performance appraisal
Quality assurance	Continuous improvement

7.1.2   Healthcare has a complex structure

Healthcare is arguably more complex than many of the industries that pioneered the use of these approaches, although many would argue that this should not mean that these approaches are not useful (Walley 2003b). Issues described by others (Benneyan & Kaminsky 1995) include the fact that healthcare practitioners believe healthcare systems are 'uniquely complex', and the process of transfer requires validation and refinement.

Juran argues that *"in the minds of many, the health industry is different. This is certainly true as to its history, technology and culture. However, the decisive factors in what works and what does not are the managerial processes, which are alike for all industries"* (Berwick, Godfrey & Roessner 1990/2002)

The complexity of ownership also leads to the lack of a top-down, or whole-system view. Any analysis incorporating a process model of inputs being transformed into outputs is complex to apply in healthcare because both the output and the customer are difficult to define.

"the product here is 'care' in both the physical and emotional senses, not a tangible physical object ... the service is delivered, or possibly co-produced, through a series of interactions between worker and patients, but the 'payer' is often far away ... leaving unclear the question of who the true customer is. Increasing productivity requires orchestrating complex interactions between professionals, service staff, agencies and clients" (Eaton 2000, p.607).

This leads to a complex performance measure system.

"Conceptually complex outputs are delivered utilising a wide variety of inputs. The measurement methodologies used are often complicated ... the output of a health system must be measured in a number of dimensions for any measurement to give a balanced and comprehensive view. These may include health outcomes, social outcomes, quality of life, and social equality as well as financial measures" (Micheli et al. 2005, p.69).

7.1.3   Healthcare is difficult and complex to change

The motivation for using these approaches in industry – primarily competition – is not present to the same degree within the NHS although it is more so in other types of healthcare system (e.g. the US). It is argued that this therefore makes sustainable change difficult to achieve. There may also be internal cultural factors: *"In healthcare, we're not that way, so you've got to be willing to change the culture. It's a bit tricky to know how hard to push... if you fail to push enough, nothing happens. If you push too hard, people will ignore what is trying to be achieved"* (Simmons 2002).

Evidence about the extent to which knowledge, theories and models from the private sector can be transferred to healthcare/public sector organisations can be found in the meta analyses reported by Golembiewski, Proehl & Sink 1982 and Robertson & Seneviratne 1995. They showed that public and private sector interventions showed similar patterns of results. However, their findings should be interpreted with care, especially given the professional nature of healthcare and the scale of the change intervention (Iles & Sutherland 2001).

However, IHI is clear that *"in matters of quality improvement, healthcare can indeed learn from industry – and perhaps, equally important, industry can also learn from healthcare. The fundamental principles of quality improvement apply to both"* (Berwick et al. 1990/2002). The issues of translation are not covered in any detail in its published work. In considering the translation of SPC (Mohammed 2004) he proposes that the fact that SPC was first used in manufacturing makes translation difficult: *"there is a reluctance, despite evidence to the contrary, to accept that an approach for improving the quality of 'widgets' can be legitimately applied to healthcare"*.

7.2 The implications for people

7.2.1 Culture

Most perspectives on improvement focus on the motivation and beliefs of individuals in the organisation, which contribute to defining the culture as well as the behaviour that results from them. Approaches to culture in the literature are ambiguous. On the one hand, some authors describe a 'quality culture' as one *"whereby everyone in the organisation shares a commitment to continuous improvement aimed at customer satisfaction"* (Wilkinson & Brown 2003, p.184). Others believe that culture cannot be 'managed' (Schein 1985) despite many policy innovations intended to achieve exactly this (Mannion, Davies & Marshall 2005).

In one study a participative, flexible, risk-taking culture was strongly associated with the implementation of quality improvement (Shortell, O'Brien, Carman et al. 1995).

7.2.2 Leadership

There are an increasing number of documents describing what leaders should do in terms of leading improvement within their organisations (Bibby & Reinertsen undated, Reinertsen, Pugh & Bisognano 2005). Many include exhortations to leaders to change the culture of their organisations (e.g. Table 21).

Table 21 – What leaders should do to change culture (Bibby & Reinertsen undated)

From	To
Unrelated pockets of improvement activity	Improvement activity aligned with measurable goals
Improvement being an add-on for enthusiasts	Improvement as a function of service delivery
Improvement stopping at organisational boundaries	Collaboration across organisations to deliver seamless care
Improvement gains confined within individual projects	Learning transferred throughout the system
Leadership of improvement as a positional responsibility	Leadership of improvement at every level of the system

Guidance from IHI states that it is based on complex system theory, observed performance of leadership and health systems as well as hunches, intuition and collective experience. It contains seven "leadership leverage points" (Reinertsen et al. 2005):

1. Establish and oversee system-level aims for improvement at the highest board and leadership level
2. Aligning system measures, strategy and projects in a leadership learning system
3. Channel leadership attention to system-level improvement
4. Get the right team on the bus
5. Make the chief financial officer a quality champion
6. Engage physicians
7. Build improvement capability.

The guidance also includes a tool for assessing performance against these points and developing desired behaviours.

A literature review of the role of managers and leaders in quality improvement (Ovretveit 2005) concluded that despite the range of literature available and the limitations of the research, there was a pattern of similar findings focused around:

- preparation – of the current state of the organisation and its improvement expertise
- vision and strategy – a vision of what the organisation should look like and an agreed and achievable strategy for reaching it
- structural and line management process changes – responsibility for quality improvement needs to be specified in job descriptions and line management processes changed to include regular reporting of quality progress
- system changes – development of data collection and reporting systems, as well as appropriate reward and incentive systems
- human resources, people and team development – training and development to support the changes required
- communication, commitment and motivation – understanding what motivates individuals, and rewards

Their guidance is summarised as:
1. Assess the situation
2. Assess your influence
3. Translate, don't transfer
4. Balance attention between the seven areas

The involvement of top management, use of teamwork and the ability to foster innovation were shown to be important in quality improvement (Parker, Wubbenhorst, Young et al. 1999). In fact, quality improvement can be seen to be dependent on leaders, both in relation to clarifying the overall mission and strategy and creating a commitment to change (Berwick et al. 1990/2002). Leaders have a key role to play in planning for quality, creating the right cultural conditions and setting organisational structures that empower staff to become actively involved in improvement (Juran 1989).

In terms of research evidence that leadership makes a difference, there is an increasing body of literature to show that it does. In terms of both clinical (outcomes) and process quality, Marley, Collier & Goldstein 2004 show that leadership is a significant influence, supporting earlier work on quality management in general (Collier, Goldstein & Wilson 2002, Flynn, Schroeder & Sakakibara 1994) as well as that specific to healthcare (Goldstein & Schweikhart 2002, Institute of Medicine & Committee on Quality Health Care in America 2001, Meyer & Collier 2001).

7.2.3   The healthcare workforce

The people implications are broader than organisational culture, relating to individual employment arrangements, professional motivation and the need to take into account both individuals and systems and the way they interact.

Concern about the impact of quality improvement initiatives on the workforce is not something unique to healthcare, nor is it an area which has received relatively much attention when compared to the details of the tools which can be used. However, it is an increasing concern, not least because *"prevailing strategies [for developing the workforce] rely largely on outmoded theories of control and standardisation of work"* (Berwick 2003 p.448). It is argued that a change in attitude is needed so that responsibility for quality is seen as something for everyone, not someone else's problem. This will then enable the workforce to *"set aims, measure and interpret results, search for unfamiliar and promising alternatives to the status quo and test those alternatives rapidly, carefully, and constantly"* (Berwick 2003 p.451) – something which is very similar to the TPS model promoted by others (Spear 2005).

However, some of the contradictions in organisational approaches to quality improvement in terms of their assumptions about the individuals who work in the organisations include (Wilkinson & Willmott 1995):

*   **the assumption that staff will welcome approaches which improve the effectiveness of the organisation:** it appears to be taken for granted by the quality gurus and their approaches that employees will welcome, and be committed to, approaches that minimise unproductive activity and enable them to take a pride in what is produced by the organisation. However, while these approaches are employed within the context of a hierarchical relationship between management and employees, the benefits from quality improvement will be limited.

- **the ownership of the organisation:** employees or managers who do not own or control the organisation that employs them are likely, according to employment research, to be concerned primarily with their own rewards and conditions of employment. However, these structures of ownership and control will also limit the extent to which employees can be involved and empowered (two aspects seen to be key to quality improvement).

- **viewing employees as internal customers:** which is a fundamental assumption of quality improvement. This is argued to be difficult to reconcile with the teamwork/empowerment approaches, which imply that individuals gain more control over their own work. The internal customer approach implies that what you produce is dictated by the requirements of your customer rather than being primarily controlled by the individual performing the work.

The Lean approach and people

A variety of authors describe in detail the implications of a Lean approach for staff within the organisation, both from Lean in general and specifically in healthcare. Early criticism of Lean production was concerned with the effect it had on the worker, arguing that Lean production meant *"a loss of autonomy and further intensification of work"* (Skorstad 1994). Other writers described Lean production as 'mean production' or 'management by stress' (Berggren 1993, Delbridge & Turnball 1992). Further work produced clearer definitions of Lean work practices (Kinnie, Hutchinson, Purcell et al. 1996, Syrett & Lammiman 1997) and defined Lean *"not as a homogeneous or invariable state but a context-dependent process"* (Kinnie et al. 1996).

However, some argue that *"Lean is not mean"* (Jones & Mitchell 2006 p.6) but it is about being able to do more with existing resources – if less people are needed they can be redeployed to create more value.

Many authors from the healthcare perspective do however highlight that job security is an issue: *"The lesson from long experience is that Lean initiatives rarely succeed unless continuity of staff employment is guaranteed in advance"* (Jones & Mitchell 2006 p.21, Thompson et al. 2003).

Many also argue that Lean will help to motivate staff and save time and money – it is *"inclusive and motivational because it encourages a problem-solving culture"* (Westwood et al. 2007 p.19) with anecdotal evidence that staff in healthcare do like the approach. The CEO of Bolton Hospitals NHS Trust suggests that Lean redesign processes have strengthened team working in those areas where relationships were already sound and helped tackle problems in areas where team working was not well established (Fillingham 2008).

Do you know what motivates the different staff groups within your organisation?
What assumptions have you made about the motivation of people
within your organisation to improve?
How can you link measures of performance to the motivating factors of
the different staff groups in the organisation?
What is likely to be the impact of short-term cost cutting and/or job security
on the success of quality improvement?

7.3   Does quality improvement work?

Many earlier publications demonstrated the extent of the issue rather than prescribing what could be done to improve quality, although these did lead to change.

Two reports on the evidence for quality failures (Hurtado et al. 2001, Kohn, Corrigan & Donaldson 1999) were catalysts for changes and improvements internationally. A book examining the 'improvement journeys' of medical organisations that have earned reputations for sustained achievement of quality improvement (Bate, Mendel & Robert 2008).

Apart from the studies on particular approaches, which are detailed earlier in this report, there are also some studies which have taken a wider remit. It is acknowledged that there is a limited number of studies, but a useful summary of *"the relatively few well-conducted empirical studies"* (Iles & Sutherland 2001) of change management within the NHS is provided in (Iles & Sutherland 2001). They cite in particular a few evaluation studies on TQM and BPR (Joss & Kogan 1995, McNulty & Ferlie 2002, Packwood, Pollitt & Roberts 1998) but reiterate the lack of research that considers the factors that shape organisational change in the NHS.

The studies that do exist have demonstrated a number of issues:

7.3.1   Methodology

In a review of reported studies evaluating the clinical application of continuous quality improvement (CQI), (Shortell, Bennett & Byck 1998) conclude that studies are limited both in terms of quantity and methodological quality. Other authors report that most studies have severe methodological limitations and that few studies describe or compare different types of programmes (Øvretveit & Gustafson 2004). This is also an issue with management research in general (Lilford, Dobbie, Warren et al. 2003) although there is acknowledgement that the speed of implementation of process redesign does hamper both longitudinal and independent research: *"the speed of implementation and the rapid proliferation of different variants…make a dispassionate assessment of its effectiveness hard to achieve"* (Locock 2003, p.122).

7.3.2 Definition

There has been such a variety of approaches to improving quality used, as well as varying understanding of what healthcare quality is that this has hampered the progress of quality improvement initiatives (Øvretveit 1997). Because of the lack of a "unified approach or common language of quality" (Øvretveit 1997), professions and departments are unable to put into practice the exhortations to work using a "systems approach". It has also been noted that the label given to a programme (for example "TQM") is no guide to the activities which are actually carried out – programmes with the same name are implemented differently at different rates, coverage and depth in the organisation (Øvretveit & Gustafson 2004)

7.3.3 Critical success factors

Those studies that have been reported provide generally favourable results in relation to the impact of CQI on clinical processes and outcomes. Critical success factors include:

- the participation of a nucleus of physicians,
- feedback to individual practitioners,
- a supportive organisational culture
- a conducive external environment (for example, alignment of policy, regulatory and incentive related factors) (Shortell et al. 1998)
- a *"phased coordinated spreading"* approach where top management monitored progress, coordinated efforts and allocated resources (Øvretveit 1997)
- although improvement activity may be bottom-up, it must be supported by *"top-down policies that are consistent with the improvement objectives"* as well as the relinquishing of some control by senior managers (Silvester et al. 2004)

Core challenges in organising for quality have been identified as shown in Table 22.

Table 22 – Core challenges to organising for quality (Bate et al. 2008)

Challenge	Lack of this can lead to …
Structural – organising, planning and coordinating quality efforts	Fragmentation and a general lack of synergy between the different parts of the organisation doing quality improvement
Political – addressing and dealing with the politics of change surrounding any quality improvement effort	Disillusionment and inertia because quality improvement is not happening on the ground, and certain groups or individuals are blocking and resisting change
Cultural – giving quality a shared, collective meaning, value and significance within the organisation	Evaporation because the change has not been properly anchored or become rooted in everyday thinking and behavioural routines
Educational – creating a learning process that supports improvement	Amnesia and frustration as lessons and knowledge are forgotten or fail to accumulate, and improvement capabilities and skills fail to keep abreast of growing aspirations
Emotional – engaging and motivating people by linking quality improvement efforts to inner sentiments and deeper commitments and beliefs	Loss of interest and fade-out as the change effort runs out of momentum due to a failure to engage front-line staff
Physical and technological – the designing of physical systems and technological infrastructure that supports and sustains quality efforts	Exhaustion as people try to make change happen informally, without a system or standardised set of routines to take the weight of necessary everyday activities

7.3.4 The process of implementation is more important than the approach

All the approaches examined are underpinned by a philosophy that quality improvement is an important value (as opposed to e.g. cost reduction) but the way in which they are implemented is vital in their success or otherwise, and should therefore be evaluated (Hackman & Wageman 1995). This view is supported by a number of other authors:

> "Most importantly, our research suggests that the inability of most organizations to reap the full benefit of these innovations has little to do with the specific improvement tool they select. Instead, the problem has its roots in how the introduction of a new improvement program Interacts with the physical, economic, social, and psychological structures in which implementation takes place. In other words, it's not just a tool problem, any more than it's a human resources problem or a leadership problem. Instead it is a systemic problem, one that is created by the interaction of tools, equipment, workers, and managers." (Repenning & Sterman 2001, p.66

"As important as the method is seriously adopting and committing to a method …
all too often the tendency has been to dabble in different methods … whatever the
flavour of the month might be" Gary Kaplan, CEO of Virginia Mason Medical
Center, quoted in (Reinertsen 2006)

A recent study of a range of quality improvement programmes (Bate et al. 2008) started
from the premise that there had been little research into how to set quality improvement
processes in motion, or into how they interrelate, leading to a focus on organising for quality.
The main conclusions of the study were that:

*"There are many different paths to successful, sustained quality improvement.
However the unifying features … are an ability to address multiple challenges
simultaneously and to adapt solutions and strategies to the organisation's own
context"* (Bate et al. 2008).

QUESTIONS TO THINK ABOUT:

How will you implement quality improvement so as to maximise the likelihood of success?
How much do you understand the system and its influence on organisational change?
Can your organisation address multiple challenges at the same time?

---

8. CONCLUSIONS

8.1 Quality improvement: the theory

8.1.1 The applicability of quality improvement approaches

There are many approaches taken, both in healthcare and industry. There is now some integration of these approaches, with a particular focus on the application of industrial approaches in healthcare. However, this raises questions about the way in which the approaches may need to be adapted for the healthcare context, and the nature of healthcare as a sector.

8.1.2 Are the approaches really different?

The various approaches appear to be different because of their historical development and labelling, although the differentiating factors are actually a matter of emphasis on the core concepts of variation, flow and customer focus. The apparent contradictions between approaches are also due to the differing assumptions about value and its definition.

All approaches are based on same principles by which organisations operate. The approaches all also draw on a fairly common body of tools for improvement, with some labelled by one approach as being an essential element. Many of these tools may be more appropriate starting points for improvement than the overall 'package'.

8.1.3 So which approach should be used?

A key challenge for organisations is to know which approach is right for them at any one point in time. To address this, organisations must define and assess the characteristics of their processes.

There is some evidence of a body of knowledge which is being built on, especially with the longer-established approaches, and many of the more recent approaches have as their foundation the statistical analysis of quality or a model of continuous and incremental improvement. However, it is difficult to argue that there is a definitive body of knowledge about any single approach and where an approach does not appear to work there are often methodological issues about the evidence to support the assertion, or concerns about whether it is too soon to assess the impact of the improvement.

8.1.4 How do we know what works?

The methods most appropriate to assess the effectiveness of quality improvement approaches is still a matter of debate, and this is likely to continue given the fundamental differences between a scientific and a social science research paradigm around the nature of proof that something works. However, key commentators are increasingly calling for more use of approaches which take into account the context for implementation; what is important is not what works, but where and why it works. Similarly, it is unlikely that there will be definitive evidence to show the optimum context for successful implementation, but as the body of evidence continues to grow the issues will become clearer.

8.1.5 Is it what works or why?

There is little guidance or evidence in the literature about practical implementation issues and in particular, the readiness of the organisation for change is rarely considered. Despite a huge amount of evidence and research on organisational change, leadership and organisational culture from the social sciences, to date this has not been incorporated to any large extent into the evidence for quality improvement.

8.2 Quality improvement: the practice

Whilst the evidence about what works, where and when with regard to any one approach is limited, there are a number of common implications for practice that can be drawn out.

8.2.1 Define quality first

Attempts to improve quality often fail to address clearly how quality is defined before starting to change organisations and processes. It is important to explore what is meant by quality before attempting to improve it – but care must also be taken to ensure that this step does not take too long.

8.2.2 Identify the process

It is clear that whatever approach is taken to improve quality, the identification of the process is a vital first step. Processes will have both clinical and organisational elements and should not be separated but integrated. Clinical processes in particular must take account of the organisational resources necessary for them to function effectively. However organisational processes must also recognise the clinical decisions which are necessary as patients go through the process. Processes are key determinants of outcomes, and their position as part of wider system must be recognised. Recognise that work is a series of processes and that organisations are part of systems – and then do something about it.

8.2.3 Beware of exclusive promotion of one approach

Whilst literature suggests that implementation is more important than the actual tool or approach chosen, this is not put across in how techniques are promoted where there is often an exclusivity about which one can or should be used. It is not clear to what extent this is the result of the people or organisations promoting particular approaches, but clearly the business mindset of consultancies that provide support for implementation to many healthcare organisations is one factor. It may be argued that there are also some academics that appear wedded to one approach/mindset and appear to show more interest in promoting pre-determined tools/approaches than solving organisational problems in the long term. The problems of the process and system should be identified before systematic change, using any approach, is undertaken. The common elements of the various approaches should also be recognised, especially at the level of tools for improvement.

8.2.4 Think about who the customer is

It must not be assumed that an individual patient is the only customer where healthcare is provided within the public sector: this is an over-simplistic approach. Other important customers include those who commission healthcare, as well as the wider public and perhaps those with political interests.

8.2.5 Understand the people

Quality will only improve where the behaviour of individuals within the system changes and this has to date often been ignored or underplayed in quality improvement efforts. Understanding what motivates the individuals within the healthcare system, especially those with a clinical professional background, is vital. A programmatic approach to improvement (e.g. we have now 'done' Lean) is not supported by the evidence: sustained improvement is about a different way of doing things, following from a changed culture and way of thinking, resulting from changes in people as well as their capability.

8.2.6 Get data about quality before you start

Data about performance and quality is needed – it should be appropriate and enable improvement action. Improvement based on gut feelings about what is wrong is not likely to be effective or sustainable. Evidence of success will not be obtained without a baseline against which to assess progress. For this reason, the define or plan stage of any approach is important so that there a basis for change.

8.2.7 Recognise the importance of whole system leadership

Organisations and whole health systems need to be effectively led and staff empowered to improve quality. Quality will not improve throughout the system when the actions or words of those at the top do not support quality improvement. Effective change will only be achieved with whole systems approaches. A piecemeal approach is limited in its impact despite short-term gains being apparent; in the long-term improvement has to be an integral part of what the organisation does, not an add-on. This means that targets for performance have to be translated into meaningful measures for different stakeholders.

REFERENCES

Addicott, R, Ferlie, E (2007) Understanding power relationships in health care networks, *Journal of Health Organization and Management,* 21 (4/5): 393-405

Addicott, R, McGivern, G, Ferlie, E (2006) Networks, organizational learning and knowledge management: NHS Cancer Networks, *Public Money and Management*, 26 (2): 87-94

Anonymous (2000) Management strategy proves effective in patient financial services, *Receivables Report for America's Health Care Financial Managers,* 15 (12): 2

Anonymous (2003) Six Sigma-for success in health care, *Quality Progress*, 36 (9): Sep 67

Antony, J (2004) Some pros and cons of Six Sigma: an academic perspective, *The TQM Magazine,* 16 (4): 303-306

Antony, J, Antony, F J, Kumar, M, Cho, B R (2007a) Six Sigma in service organisations: benefits challenges and difficulties, common myths, empirical observations and success factors, *International Journal of Quality & Reliability Management*, 24 (3): 294-311

Antony, J, Downey-Ennis, K, Antony, F, Seow, C (2007b) Can Six Sigma be the "cure" for our "ailing" NHS? *Leadership in Health Services*, 20 (4): 242-253

Arah, O A, Klazinga, N S, Delnoij, D M J, Asbroek, A H A T, Custers, T (2003) Conceptual frameworks for health systems performance: a quest for effectiveness, quality, and improvement, *International Journal for Quality in Health Care,* 15 (5): October 1 377-398

Armistead, C G, Clarke, G (1994) The 'coping' capacity management strategy in services and the influence on quality performance, *International Journal of Service Industry Management*, 5 (2): 5-22

Arndt, M, Bigelow, B (1995) The implementation of total quality management in hospitals: how good is the fit? *Health Care Management Review*, 20 (4): Fall 7-14

Arnheiter, E D, Maleyeff, J (2005) The integration of Lean management and Six Sigma, *The TQM Magazine*, 17 (1): 5-18

Audit Commission (2003). *Acute hospital portfolio (phase 3): Bed management - review of national findings*. London: Audit Commission.

Bagust, A, Place, M, Posnett, J (1999) Dynamics of bed use in accommodating emergency admissions: stochastic simulation model, *British Medical Journal*, 319 155-158

Balestracci, D (1998). *Data sanity: statistical thinking applied to everyday data, Special Publication of the American Society for Quality Statistics Division*.

Banuelas, R, Antony, J (2002) Critical success factors for the successful implementation of Six Sigma projects in organisations, *The TQM Magazine*, 14 (2): 92-99

Barry, R, Smith, A C. (2005). *The manager's guide to Six Sigma in healthcare; practical tips and tools for improvement Milwaukee*, WI: ASQ Quality Press.

Barry, R B, Murcko, A, Brubaker, C. (2002) *The Six Sigma book for healthcare:* ASQ Quality Press.

Bate, P, Mendel, P, Robert, G. (2008). *Organizing for quality*. Oxford: Radcliffe.

Bate, S P, Robert, G (2002) Knowledge management and communities of practice in the private sector: lessons for modernising the NHS in England and Wales, *Public Administration*, 80 (4): 643-663

Bate, S P, Robert, G, McLeod, H (2002). *Report on the 'Breakthrough' Collaborative approach to quality and service improvement within four regions of the NHS. A research based investigation of the Orthopaedic Services Collaborative within the Eastern, South and West, South East and Trent regions.* Birmingham: University of Birmingham: Health Services Management Centre.

Ben-Tovim, D I, Bassham, J E, Bennett, D M, Dougherty, M L, Martin, M A, O'Neill, S J, Sincock, J L, Szwarcbord, M G (2008a) Redesigning care at the Flinders medical centre: clinical process redesign using "Lean thinking", *Medical Journal of Australia*, 188 (6 Supplement): S27-S31

Ben-Tovim, D I, Bassham, J E, Bolch, D, Martin, M A, Dougherty, M, Szwarcbord, M (2007) Lean thinking across a hospital: redesigning care at the Flinders medical centre, *Australian Health Review*, 31 (1): Feb 10-15

Ben-Tovim, D I, Dougherty, M L, O'Connell, T J, McGrath, K M (2008b) Patient journeys: the process of clinical redesign, *Medical Journal of Australia*, 188 (6 Supplement): S14-S17

Bendell, T, Penson, R, Carr, S (1995) The quality gurus - their approaches described and considered, *Managing Service Quality*, 5 (6): 44-48

Benedetto, A R (2003a) Adapting manufacturing-based Six Sigma methodology to the service environment of a radiology film library, *Journal of Healthcare Management*, 48 (4): Jul/Aug 263

Benedetto, A R (2003b) Six Sigma: not for the faint of heart, *Radiology Management*, 25 (2): Mar/April 40-53

Benner, M J, Tushman, M L (2003) Exploitation, exploration, and process management: The productivity dilemma revisited, *The Academy of Management Review*, 28 (2): 238-256

Benneyan, J C, Kaminsky, F C (1995) Another view on how to measure health care quality, *Quality Progress*, 28 (2): 120-125

Benneyan, J C, Lloyd, R C, Plsek, P E (2003) Statistical process control as a tool for research and healthcare improvement, *Quality and Safety in Health Care*, 12 (6): December 458-464

Benneyan, J C, Lloyd, R C, Plsek, P E. (2004) Statistical process control as a tool for research and healthcare improvement. In R. B. R Grol, F Moss (Ed.), *Quality Improvement Research*. London: BMJ Books: 184-202

Berggren, C (1993) Lean production – the end of history *Work, Employment and Society*, 7 (2): 163-188

Berry, L L, Zeithaml, V A, Parasuraman, A (1985) Quality counts in services too, *Business Horizons*, 28 (3): 44-52

Berwick, D (1991) Controlling variation in healthcare: a consultation from Walter Shewhart, *Medical Care*, 29 1212-1225

Berwick, D (1997) The total customer relationship in health care: broadening the bandwidth, *Joint Commission Journal on Quality Improvement*, 23 (5): May 245-250

Berwick, D M (1989) Continuous improvement as an ideal in healthcare, *New England Journal of Medicine*, 320 (1): 53-56

Berwick, D M (2003) Improvement, trust, and the healthcare workforce, *Quality and Safety in Health Care*, 6 (6): Dec 2-7

Berwick, D M (2005) The John Eisenberg Lecture: Health services research as a citizen in improvement, *Health Services Research*, 40 (2): April 01, 2005 317-336

Berwick, D M (2008) The science of improvement, *JAMA*, 299 (10): March 12 1182-1184

Berwick, D M, Endhoven, A, Bunker, J P (1992) Quality management in the NHS: the doctor's role, *BMJ*, 304 (6822): 304-308

Berwick, D M, Godfrey, A B, Roessner, J. (1990/2002). *Curing health care* (paperback edition July 2002 Ed.). San Francisco: Jossey-Bass.

Bhasin, S, Burcher, P (2006) Lean viewed as a philosophy, *Journal of Manufacturing Technology Management*, 17 (1): 56-72

Bibby, J, Reinertsen, J L (undated). *Leading for improvement - whose job is it anyway?* NHS Modernisation Agency.

Bicheno, J. (2000). *The Lean toolbox*. Buckingham: PICSIE Books.

Bicheno, J. (2002). The Quality 75: *Towards Six Sigma performance in service and manufacturing*. Buckingham: PICSIE Books.

Black, K, Revere, L (2006) Six Sigma arises from the ashes of TQM with a twist, *International Journal of Health Care Quality Assurance*, 19 (3): 259-266

Blumenthal, D (1996) Quality of care - what is it? - Part One of Six, *New England Journal of Medicine*, 335 (12): September 19, 1996 891-894

Boaden, R, Proudlove, N, Wilson, M (1999) An exploratory study of bed management, *Journal of Management in Medicine*, 13 (4): 234-250

Bossert, J (2003) Lean and Six Sigma – synergy made in heaven, *Quality Progress*, 36 (7):

Boynton, A C, Victor, B, Pine, B J (1993) New competitive strategies: challenges to organizations and information technology, *IBM Systems Journal*, 32 (1): 40-64

Brady, J E, Allen, T T (2006) Six Sigma literature: a review and agenda for future research, *Quality and Reliability Engineering International*, 22 (3): 335 - 367

Brantes, F D, Galvin, R S (2001) Creating, connecting and supporting active consumers, *International Journal of Medical Marketing*, 2 (1): 8

Brassard, M, Finn, L, Ginn, D, Ritter, D. (2002) *The Six Sigma Memory Jogger* Salem: GOAL/QPC.

Breen, A, Burton-Houle, T, Aron, D (2002) Applying the theory of constraints in health care: Part 1 - the philosophy, *Quality Management in Health Care*, 10 (3): 40-46

Breyfogle III, F W, Cupello, J M, Meadows, B. (2001). *Managing Six Sigma.* New York: John Wiley and Sons Inc

Brideau, L P (2004) Flow: why does it matter? *Frontiers of Health Services Management*, 20 (4): Summer 47-50

Brock, D M, Powell, M J, Hinings, C R (Eds.) (1999) Restructuring the professional organization: *Accounting, health care and law.* London: Routledge.

Buchanan, D (1997) The limitations and opportunities of business process reengineering in a politicized organisational climate, *Human Relations*, 50 (1): 51-72

Buchanan, D, Fitzgerald, L, Ketley, D. (2007). *The sustainability and spread of organizational change.* Abingdon: Routledge.

Buck, C R (1998) Health care through a Six Sigma lens, *The Milbank Quarterly*, 76 (4): 749-753

Bush, R W (2007) Reducing waste in US health care systems, *JAMA*, 297 (8): February 28, 2007 871-874

Bushell, S, Mobley, J, Shelest, B (2002) Discovering Lean thinking at Progressive Healthcare, *The Journal for Quality and Participation*, 25 (2): 20-25

Campbell, M, Fitzpatrick, R, Haines, A, Kinmonth, A L, Sandercock, R, Spiegelhalter, D, Tyrer, P (2000) Framework for design and evaluation of complex interventions to improve health, *BMJ*, 321 (7262): 694-696

Carey, R G. (2002) *Improving healthcare with control charts.* Milwaukee, MI.: ASQ Quality Press.

Caulcutt, R (2001) Why is Six Sigma so successful? *Journal of Applied Statistics*, 28 (3): 301-306

Chaplin, E. (2003). *The application of Six Sigma strategies to medication administration,* Paper presented at the Quality Congress. ASQ's Annual Quality Congress Proceedings

Chassin, M (1998) Is health care ready for Six Sigma quality? *The Milbank Quarterly*, 76 (4): 565-591

Checkland, P. (1981). *Systems thinking, systems practice.* New York: John Wiley.

Clarke, C L, Reed, J, Wainwright, D, McClelland, S, Swallow, V, Harden, J, Walton, G, Walsh, A (2004) The discipline of improvement: something old, something new? *Journal of Nursing Management*, 12 (2): 85-96

Codman, E A. (1916) *A Study in hospital efficiency: the first five years*. Boston: Thomas Todd Co.

Collier, D A, Goldstein, S M, Wilson, D D (2002) Building a model of organization performance grounded in the Baldrige Award Criteria, *Quality Progress*, 35 (10): 97-104

Conyon, I. (2006). *The management of hospital bed resources: an operations management perspective*. University of Manchester, Manchester

Cooper, A H. (2002) Six Sigma deployment in a large integrated healthcare system. Paper presented at the ASQ's Annual Quality Congress Proceedings 71-77

Cooper, J B, Sorensen, A V, Anderson, S M, Zipperer, L A, Blum, L N, Blim, J F (2001). *Current research on patient safety in the United States*. Chicago: National Patient Safety Foundation.

Crombie, I K, Davies, H T O (1998) Beyond health outcomes: the advantages of measuring process, *Journal of Evaluation in Clinical Practice*, 4 (1): 31-38

Dahlgaard, S M P (1999) The evolution patterns of quality management: Some reflections on the quality movement, *Total Quality Management*, 10 (4/5): Jul 473-481

Dale, B G (Ed.) (2003) *Managing Quality* (4th Ed.). Oxford: Blackwell.

Davids, M (1999) W Edwards Deming (1900-1993): Quality controller, *The Journal of Business Strategy*, 20 (5): Sep/Oct 31

Davies, C, Walley, P (2000) Clinical governance and operations management methodologies, *International Journal of Health Care and Quality Assurance*, 13 (1): 21-26

Davies, H T O, Mannion, R, Jacobs, R, Powell, A E, Marshall, M N (2007) Exploring the relationship between senior management team culture and hospital performance, *Medical Care Research and Review*, 64 (1): Feb 46-65

de Koning, H, Verver, J P S, van den Heuvel, J, Bisgaard, S, Does, R J M M (2006) Lean Six Sigma in healthcare, *Journal for Healthcare Quality*, 28 (2): 4–11

Delbridge, R, Turnball, P. (1992). Human resource maximisation: the management of labour under just-in-time manufacturing systems. In P. Blyton, & P. Turnball (Eds.), *Reassessing Human Resource Management* London: Sage

Deming, W E. (1986) *Out of the crisis*. Cambridge, Mass.: Centre of Advanced Engineering Study, MIT.

Department of Health (1989) *Working for Patients: Medical Audit (Working Paper No.6)*. London: HMSO.

Department of Health (2000) *The NHS Cancer Plan. A plan for investment, a plan for reform* London: HMSO.

Department of Health (2004) *Transforming emergency care* - a report by Professor Sir George Alberti

Donabedian, A (1966) Evaluating the quality of medical care, *Milbank Memorial Fund Quarterly*, 44 (3, Part 2): 166-206

Donabedian, A. (1980). Explorations in quality assessment and monitoring, *Volume 1: The definition of quality and approaches to its assessment*. Ann Arbor, Michigan: Health Administration Press.

Donabedian, A (1987) Commentary on some studies of the quality of care, *Health Care Financing Review*, Annual Supplement December 75-86

Donabedian, A (1988) The quality of care: how can it be assessed? *JAMA*, 260 (12): September 23, 1988: 1743-1748

Duff, L A, Kitson, A L, Seers, K, Humphris, D (1996) Clinical guidelines: an introduction to their development and implementation, *Journal of Advanced Nursing*, 23 (5): 887-895

Eaton, S C (2000) Beyond `unloving care': linking human resource management and patient care quality in nursing homes, *International Journal of Human Resource Management?* 11 (3): 591-616

Erwin, J, Douglas, P (2000) Six Sigma's focus on total customer satisfaction, *The Journal for Quality and Participation*, 23 (2): 45-49

Esain, A, Angel, L, Robertson, K. (2006) The application of Six Sigma within healthcare In K. Mendibil, & A. Shamsuddin (Eds.), *Proceedings of the European Operations Management Association (EUROMA) Conference*, Vol. 2. University of Strathclyde, Glasgow: 829-838

Esimai, G (2005) Lean Six Sigma reduces medication errors, *Quality Progress*, 38 (4): April 51-57

Ettinger, W, Kooy, M V (2003) The art and science of winning physician support for Six Sigma change, *The Physician Executive*, Sep/Oct 34-38

Ettinger, W H (2001) Six Sigma: Adapting GE's lessons to healthcare, Trustee, 54 (8): Sep 10-14

European Foundation for Quality Management (1999) *Assessing for Excellence: A Practical Guide for Self-Assessment*. Brussels: EFQM.

Ferlie, E, Aggarwal, K, McGivern, G (2002). *Assessing the impact of large-scale quality-led change programmes: a scoping document.* London: Imperial College Management School.

Fillingham, D (2007) Can Lean save lives? *Leadership in Health Services*, 20 (4): 231-241

Fillingham, D (2008) *Lean healthcare, improving the patient's experience.* Chichester: Kingsham Press

Fitzgerald, C Q, McLaughlin, C P (2001) Custom medicine for the masses, *Pharmaceutical Executive*, 21 (12): 64-68

Flamm, B, Berwick, D, Kabcenell, A (1998) Reducing caesarean section rates safely: lessons from a 'breakthrough series' collaborative, *Birth*, 25 (2): 117-124

Flood, A B (1994) The impact of organizational and managerial factors on the quality of care in health care organizations, *Medical Care Review*, 51 (4): 381 - 428

Florin, D, Rosen, R (1999) Evaluating NHS Direct: early findings raise questions about expanding the service, *BMJ*, 319 (7201): 5-6

Flynn, B, Sakakibara, S, Schroeder, R G (1995) Relationship between JIT and TQM: practices and performance, *Academy of Management Journal*, 38 (5): 1325-1360

Flynn, B, Schroeder, R G, Sakakibara, S (1994) A framework for quality management research and an associated measurement instrument, *Journal of Operations Management*, 11 (4): 339-366

Forthman, M T, Wooster, L D, Hill, W C, Homa-Lowry, J M, DesHarnais, S I (2003) Insights into successful change management: empirically supported techniques for improving medical practice patterns, *American Journal of Medical Quality*, 18 (5): 181-189

Frings, G, Grant, L (2005) Who moved my sigma... effective implementation of the Six Sigma methodology to hospitals, *Quality and Reliability Engineering International*, 21 (3): 311-328

Gabor, A. (1990). *The Man Who Discovered Quality*. New York: Times Books Division of Random House.

Garvin, D. (1988). *Managing Quality - the strategic and competitive edge*. New York: Free Press.

Gemmel, P, Van Dierdonck, R (1999) Admission scheduling in acute care hospitals: Does practice fit with theory? *International Journal of Operations and Production Management*, 19 (9): 863-878

George, M L. (2003). *Lean Six Sigma for service*. New York: McGraw Hill.

George, M L, Rowlands, D. (2003). *What is Lean Six Sigma?* New York: McGraw-Hill Education.

George, M L, Rowlands, D, Price, M, Maxey, J. (2005). *The Lean Six Sigma pocket toolbook*. New York: McGraw-Hill.

Gilmore, J H, Pine II, B J (1997) The four faces of mass customization, *Harvard Business Review*, 75 (1): Jan/Feb 91-101

Giuffrida, A, Gravelle, H, Roland, M (1999) Measuring quality of care with routine data: avoiding confusion between performance indicators and health outcomes, *BMJ*, 319 (7202): July 10, 1999 94-98

Goddard, M, Mannion, R, Smith, P C (1999) Assessing the performance of NHS Hospital Trusts: the role of 'hard' and 'soft' information, *Health Policy*, 48 (2): 119-134

Goldratt, E, Cox, J. (1984). *The Goal* (2nd ed.). Aldershot: Gower.

Goldratt, E M (1988) Computerised shop floor scheduling, *International Journal of Production Research*, 26 (3): 453

Goldratt, E M. (1997). *Critical chain*. Great Barrington, MA, USA: The North River Press.

Goldratt Group and Oxford Radcliffe Hospitals NHS Trust (2003). *The Oxford story*: 17: Goldratt Group and Oxford Radcliffe Hospitals NHS Trust.

Goldstein, S M, Schweikhart, S B (2002) Empirical support for the Baldrige award framework in US hospitals, *Health Care Management Review*, 27 (1): 62-75

Golembiewski, R, Proehl, C, Sink, D (1982) Estimating the success of OD applications, *Training and Development Journal*, 36 (4): April 94-95

Goode, J, Greatbatch, D (2005) Boundary work: The production and consumption of health information and advice within service interactions between staff and callers to NHS Direct, *Journal of Consumer Culture*, 5 315-337

Grazier, K (2003) Editorial, *Journal of Healthcare Management*, 48 (6): Nov/Dec 3/4

Grim, S (2001) Six Sigma business strategy aims at improving quality of care, *Journal of Healthcare Compliance*, 3 (3): May/June 2

Grimshaw, J M, Thomas, R E, Maclennan, G, Fraser, C, R, R C, Vale, L (2004) Effectiveness and efficiency of guidelines dissemination and implementation strategies, *Health Technology Assessment*, 8 (6): 1-72

Grol, R, Baker, R, Moss, F (Eds.). (2004). *Quality improvement research: understanding the science of change in health care*. London: BMJ Books.

Grol, R, Berwick, D M, Wensing, M (2008) On the trail of quality and safety in health care, *BMJ*, 336 (7635): January 12, 2008 74-76

Groonroos, C. (1984). *Strategic Management and Marketing in the Service Sector*. London: Chartwell-Bratt.

Hackman, J R, Wageman, R (1995) Total quality management: Empirical, conceptual and practical issues, *Administrative Science Quarterly*, 40 (2): June 309-342

Hammer, M, Champy, J. (1993). *Reengineering the corporation: a manifesto for business revolution*. New York: Harper Collins.

Haraden, C, Resar, R (2004) Patient flow in hospitals: Understanding and controlling it better, *Frontiers of Health Services Management*, 20 (4): Summer 3-15

Harry, M J, Schroeder, R. (1999). *Six Sigma: the breakthrough management strategy revolutionising the world's top corporations*. New York: Doubleday.

Harvey, G (1996) Quality in Health Care: Traditions, influences and future directions, *International Journal for Quality in Health Care*, 8 (4): 341-350

Healthcare Commission (2006a). *Acute hospital portfolio review: Management of admission in acute hospitals - Review of the national findings – 2006*. London: Healthcare Commission.

Healthcare Commission (2006b). *Investigation into outbreaks of Clostridium difficile at Stoke Mandeville Hospital, Buckinghamshire Hospitals NHS Trust*. London: Commission for Healthcare Audit and Inspection.

Healthcare Commission (2008). *Learning from investigations.* London: Healthcare Commission.

Heineke, J (1995) Strategic operations management decisions and professional performance in U.S. HMOs, *Journal of Operations Management*, 13 (4): 255-272

Hines, P, Holweg, M, Rich, N (2004) Learning to evolve: a review of contemporary Lean thinking, *International Journal of Operations and Production Management*, 24 (10): 994-1011

Hines, P, Rich, N (1997) The seven value stream mapping tools, *International Journal of Operations and Production Management*, 17 (1): 46-54

Horbar, J, Rogowski, J, Plsek, P (2001) Collaborative quality improvement for neonatal intensive care, *Pediatrics*, 107 (1): Jan 14-22

Horton, S (2004) Increasing capacity while improving the bottom line, *Frontiers of Health Services Management*, 20 (4): Summer 17-23

Huczynski, A. (1993). *Management gurus.* London: Routledge.

Hurtado, M P, Swift, E K, Corrigan, J M (Eds.). (2001). *Crossing the quality chasm.* Washington DC: Institute of Medicine.

Hutchins, D (2000) The power of Six Sigma in practice, *Quality Focus*, 4 (2): Second quarter 26-24

Iles, V, Sutherland, K (2001). *Organisational change: a review for health care managers, professionals and researchers.* London: National Co-ordinating Centre for NHS Service Delivery and Organisation Research and Development.

Institute for Healthcare Improvement (2003). *Optimizing patient flow: moving patients smoothly through acute care settings.* Boston: Institute for Health Improvement.

Institute for Medicine. (1992). *Guidelines for clinical practice: from development to use.* Washington D.C.: National Academy Press.

Jacobs, R, Goddard, M, Smith, P (2007). Public Services: are composite measures a robust reflection of performance in the public sector?, *Centre for Health Economics Research Policy Discussion Briefing*: University of York.

Jacobs, R, Martin, S, Goddard, M, Gravelle, H, Smith, P (2006) Exploring the determinants of NHS performance ratings: lessons for performance assessment systems, *Journal of Health Services Research and Policy*, 11 (4): 211-217

James, B (2005) At the crossroads of quality, *Hospitals and Health Networks*, 79 (7): 142

Jimmerson, C, Weber, D, Sobek, D K (2005) Reducing waste and errors: piloting lean principles at Intermountain Healthcare, *Joint Commission Journal on Quality and Patient Safety*, 31 (5): 249-257

Johnston, R, Clark, G. (2005). *Service operations management: Improving service delivery.* Harlow: Prentice Hall.

Johnstone, P, Hendrickson, J, Derbach, A, Secord, A, Parker, J, Favata, M, Puckett, M (2003) Ancillary services in health care industry: is Six Sigma reasonable? *Quality Management in Health Care*, 12 (1): Jan-March 11

Jones, D T (2006) Leaning healthcare, *Management Services*, 50 (2): Summer 16-17

Jones, D T, Mitchell, A (2006). *Lean Thinking for the NHS,* NHS Confederation Leading Edge Reports. London: NHS Confederation.

Jones, R, Joy, M P, Pearson, J (2002) Forecasting demand of emergency care, *Health Care Management Science*, 5 (4): Nov 297-305

Joss, R, Kogan, M. (1995). *Advancing quality: Total Quality Management in the NHS.* Buckingham: Open University Press.

Juran Institute. (2005). *Lean Six Sigma training programme*. Leicester.

Juran, J (Ed.). (1951). *The quality control handbook* (4th ed.). New York: McGraw Hill.

Juran, J. (1989). *Juran on leadership for quality*. New York: Free Press.

Kaplan, G S, Rona, J M. (2004). Seeking zero defects: applying the Toyota Production System to health care. Paper presented at the 16th National Forum on Quality Improvement in Healthcare, *Orlando, Florida*.12-15 Dec

Kennedy, I (2001). *Learning from Bristol: the report of the public enquiry into children's heart surgery at the Bristol Royal Infirmary*, 1984-1995. London: Command Paper cm 5207.

Kenney, C. (2008). *The best practice: how the new quality movement in transforming medicine.* New York: Public Affairs, Perseus Books Group.

Kerr, D, Bevan, H, Gowland, B, Penny, J, Berwick, D (2002) Redesigning cancer care, *BMJ,* 324 (7330): 164-167

Kershaw, R (2000) Using ToC to "cure" healthcare problems, *Management Accounting Quarterly*, 1 (7): Spring 1-7

Kilo, C M (1998) A framework for collaborative improvement: Lessons learned from the Institute of Healthcare Improvement's Breakthrough Series, *Quality Management in Healthcare*, 6 (4): 1-13

Kim, C S, Spahlinger, D A, Kin, J M, Billi, J E (2006) Lean health care: What can hospitals learn from a world-class automaker?, *Journal of Hospital Medicine*, 1 (3): 191-199

Kinnie, N, Hutchinson, S, Purcell, J, Rees, C, Scarbrough, H, Terr, M (1996). *The people management implications of Leaner working*. London: Institute of Personnel Management.

Klefsjö, B, Wiklund, H, Edgeman, R L (2001) Six Sigma seen as a methodology for total quality management, *Measuring Business Excellence*, 5 (1): 31-35

Knight, A (2000/1) Healing the National Health Service, *The Ashridge Journal*, Winter 8-15

Kohn, L T, Corrigan, J M, Donaldson, M S (Eds.). (1999). *To err is human: building a safer health system.* Washington D.C.: Institute of Medicine.

Kolb, D A. (1984). *Experiential learning: Experience as the source of learning and development*. New York: Prentice Hall.

Kolesar, P J (1993) The relevance of research on statistical process control to the total quality movement, *Journal of Engineering and Technology Management*, 10 (4): 1993/12 317-338

Kollberg, B, Dahlgaard, J, Brehmer, P (2007) Measuring Lean thinking initiatives in health care services: issues and findings, *International Journal of Productivity and Performance Management*, 56 (1): 7-24

Langley, G J, Nolan, K M, Nolan, T W, Norman, L, Provost, L P. (1996). *The improvement guide*. San Francisco: Jossey-Bass.

Lanham, B, Maxson-Cooper, P (2003) Is Six Sigma the answer for nursing to reduce medical errors and enhance patient safety? *Nursing Economics*, 21 (1): Jan/Feb 39-41

Larson, J S, Muller, A (2002/3) Managing the quality of healthcare, *Journal of Health and Health Services Administration*, 25 (3/4): Winter 261-280

Laux, D T (2008) *Six Sigma evolution clarified - Letter to the editor* http://www.isixsigma.com/library/content/c020131a.asp [accessed 1 April 2008]

Lazarus, I R (2003) Six sigma: Raising the bar, *Managed Healthcare Executive*, 13 (1): Jan 31-34

Lazarus, I R, Stamps, B (2002) The promise of Six Sigma (part 2), *Managed Healthcare Executive*, 12 (1): 27-30

Leape, L, Kabcenell, A, Gandhi, T (2000) Reducing adverse drug events: lessons from a breakthrough series collaborative, *Joint Commission Journal on Quality Improvement*, 26 (6): 321-331

Leese, B, Heywood, P, Allgar, V, Walker, R, Darr, A, Din, I (2006) Developing cancer services strategy in primary care in England: Primary care trust managers' views of the primary care cancer leads initiative, *Journal of Health Organization and Management*, 20 (2): 140-149

Lepore, D, Cohen, O. (1999). *Deming and Goldratt: the Theory of Constraints and the system of profound knowledge.* Great Barrington, MA: North River Press.

Li, L X, Benton, W C, Keong Leong, G (2002) The impact of strategic operations management decisions on community hospital performance, *Journal of Operations Management*, 20 389-408

Liker, J. (2004). T*he Toyota Way: 14 management principles from the world's greatest manufacturer.* New York: Mc-Graw Hill.

Lilford, R, Mohammed, M A, Spiegelhalter, D, Thomson, R (2004) Use and misuse of process and outcome data in managing performance of acute medical care: avoiding institutional stigma, *The Lancet*, 363 (9415): 1147-1154

Lilford, R J (2003). *The Director's statement, patient safety research programme in England.* Birmingham: University of Birmingham.

Lilford, R J, Dobbie, F, Warren, R, Braunholtz, D, Boaden, R (2003) Top-rated British business research: has the emperor got any clothes? *Health Services Management Research*, 16 (3): 147-154

Linderman, K, Schroeder, R G, Zaheer, S, Choo, A S (2003) Six Sigma: a goal-theoretic perspective, *Journal of Operations Management*, 21 (2): 193-203

Locock, L (2003) Healthcare redesign: meaning, origins and application, *Quality and Safety in Health Care*, 12 (1): 53-58

Lovelock, C. (1992). Strategies for managing capacity-constrained resources. In L. C (Ed.), *Managing Services: Marketing, operations and human resources.* Englewood Cliffs: Prentice Hall

Lubitsh, G, Doyle, C E, Valentine, J (2005) The impact of Theory of Constraints (ToC) in an NHS Trust, *Journal of Management Development*, 24 (2): 116-131

Lucier, G T, Seshadri, S (2001) GE takes Six Sigma beyond the bottom line, *Strategic Finance*, 82 (11): May 40

Lugon, M, Secker-Walker, J (Eds.). (1999). *Clinical Governance: making it happen.* London: Royal Society of Medicine Press.

Mabin, V J, Balderstone, S J (2003) The performance of the Theory of Constraints methodology: Analysis and discussion of successful TOC applications, *International Journal of Operations & Production Management*, 23 (6): 568 -- 595

MacLellan, D G, Cregan, P C, McCaughan, B C, O'Connell, T J, McGrath, K M (2008) Applying clinical process redesign methods to planned arrivals in New South Wales hospitals, *Medical Journal of Australia*, 188 (6 Supplement): S23-S26

Mango, P D, Shapiro, L A (2001) Hospitals get serious about operations, *McKinsey Quarterly*, (issue 2): 74-85

Manning-Courtney, P (2007) Addressing the crisis in access to autism treatment using health care improvement science, *Archives of Pediatrics & Adolescent Medicine*, 161 (4): Apr 414-415

Mannion, R, Davies, H T O, Marshall, M N. (2005). *Cultures for performance in health care.* Maidenhead: Open University Press.

Manos, A, Sattler, M, Alukal, G (2006) Make healthcare Lean, *Quality Progress*, 39 (7): July 24-30

Marley, K A, Collier, D A, Goldstein, S M (2004) The role of clinical and process quality in achieving patient satisfaction in hospitals, *Decision Sciences*, 35 (3): Summer 349-369

Marshall, M N, Shekelle, P G, Leatherman, S, Brook, R H (2000) The public release of performance data: What do we expect to gain? A review of the evidence, *JAMA*, 283 (14): April 12, 2000 1866-1874

Marshall, T, Mohammed, M A, Rouse, A (2004) A randomized controlled trial of league tables and control charts as aids to health service decision-making, *International Journal of Quality in Health Care*, 16 (4): August 1, 2004 309-315

Marti, F (2005) Lean Six Sigma method in phase 1 clinical trials: A practical example, *The Quality Assurance Journal*, 9 (1): 35-39

Martinez-Lorente, A R, Dewhurst, F, Dale, B G (1998) Total Quality Management: origins and evolution of the term, *The TQM Magazine*, 10 (5): 378-386

Mathieson, S (2006) Wait watchers, *Health Services Journal*, 16 Mar S4-S5

Maxwell, R J (1984) Quality assessment in health, *British Medical Journal*, 288 (6428): 1470-1472

McAdam, R, Lafferty, B (2004) A multilevel case study critique of Six Sigma: statistical control or strategic change? *International Journal of Operations and Production Management*, 24 (5): 530-549

McBryde, V E (1986) In today's market: quality is best focal point for upper management, *Industrial Engineering*, 18 (7): 51-55

McGrath, K M, Bennett, D M, Ben-Tovim, D I, Boyages, S C, Lyons, N J, O'Connell, T J (2008) Implementing and sustaining transformational change in health care: lessons learnt about clinical process redesign, *Medical Journal of Australia*, 188 (6 Supplement): S32-S35

McKone, K E, Schroeder, R G, Cua, K O (2001) The impact of total productive maintenance practices on manufacturing performance, *Journal of Operations Management*, 19 (1): 39-58

McLaughlin, C P (1996) Why variation reduction is not everything: a new paradigm for service operations, *international Journal of Service Industry Management*, 7 (3): 17-30

McLaughlin, C P, Kaluzny, A D (1997) Total Quality Management issues in managed care, *Journal of Health Care Finance*, 24 (1): 10-16

McLaughlin, C P, Kaluzny, A D (2000) Building client centred systems of care: Choosing a process direction for the next century, *Health Care Management Review*, 25 (1): Winter 73

McLaughlin, C P, Simpson, K N. (1999). Does TQM/CQI work in healthcare? In C. P. McLaughlin, & A. D. Kaluzny (Eds.), *Continuous Quality Improvement in Health Care: Theory, Implementation and Applications*. Gaithersburg: Aspen.

McNulty, T, Ferlie, E. (2002). *Reengineering health care: the complexities of organisational transformation*. Oxford: Oxford University Press.

Merry, P, Wing, G (1993) The Sigma Project, *International Journal of Health Care Quality Assurance*, 6 (6): 4

Meyer, J P, Allen, N J, Smith, C A (1993) Commitment to organizations and occupations: extension and test of a three-component conceptualization, *Journal of Applied Psychology*, 78 (4): August 538-551

Meyer, S M, Collier, D A (2001) An empirical test of the causal relationships in the Baldrige health care pilot criteria, *Journal of Operations Management*, 19 (4): 403-425

Micheli, P, Mason, S, Kennerley, M, Wilcox, M (2005) Public sector performance: efficiency or quality? *Measuring Business Excellence*, 9 (2): 68-73

Middleton, S, Barnett, J, Reeves, D (2001) What is an Integrated Care Pathway? *What is ...?*, 3 (3): Feb 1-8

Miller, D, (Ed) (2005). *Going Lean in healthcare*. In Institute for Healthcare Improvement (Ed.), Innovation Series. Cambridge, MA: Institute for Healthcare Improvement.

Miller, J (2003) Mass customization suits varied needs of large employers *Managed Healthcare Executive*, 13 (9): 46-47

Mintzberg, H. (1979). *The structuring of organisations*. New York: Prentice Hall.

Mohammed, M A (2004) Using statistical process control to improve the quality of health care, *Quality and Safety in Health Care*, 13 (4): August 1, 2004 243-245

Mohammed, M A, Cheng, K K, Rouse, A, Marshall, T (2001) Bristol, Shipman, and clinical governance: Shewhart's forgotten lessons, *The Lancet*, 357 (9254): 2001/2/10 463-467

Mohammed, M A, Laney, D (2006) Overdispersion in health care performance data: Laney's approach, *Quality and Safety in Health Care*, 15 383-384

Mohammed, M A, Rathbone, A, Myers, P, Patel, D, Onions, H, Stevens, A (2004) An investigation into general practitioners associated with high patient mortality flagged up through the Shipman inquiry: retrospective analysis of routine data, *BMJ*, 328 (7454): June 19, 2004 1474-1477

Mohammed, M A, Worthington, P, Woodall, W H (2008) Plotting basic control charts: tutorial notes for healthcare practitioners, *Quality and Safety in Health Care*, 17 (2): April 1, 2008 137-145

Montgomery, D C. (2001). *Introduction to Statistical Quality Control* (4th ed.). NY: Wiley.

Morrell, C, Harvey, G, Kitson, A L (1997) Practitioner based quality improvement: a review of the Royal College of Nursing's dynamic standards setting system, *Quality in Health Care*, 6 (1): 29-34

Morrell, D, Green, J, Armstrong, D, Bartholomew, J, Gelder, F, Jenkins, C, Jankowski, R, Mandalia, S, Britten, N, Shaw, A, Savill, R (Eds.). (1994). *Five essays on emergency pathways.* London: Kings Fund.

Naisbitt, J. (2001). *High Tech/High Touch: Technology and our accelerated search for meaning,* Nicholas Brealey Publishing Ltd.

National Audit Office (2000). *Inpatient admissions and bed management in NHS acute hospitals*, HC 254 Session 1999-2000. London: HMSO.

Nave, D (2002) How to compare Six Sigma, Lean and the Theory of Constraints, *Quality Progress*, 35 (3): March 73-78

Nelson-Peterson, D L, Leppa, C J (2007) Creating an environment for caring using Lean principles of the Virginia Mason Production System, *Journal of Nursing Administration*, 37 (6): Jun 287-294

NHS Institute for Innovation and Improvement (2006). *Lean Six Sigma: some basic concepts*. Coventry: NHS Institute for Innovation and Improvement.

NHS Institute for Innovation and Improvement (2007) *Lean Thinking Slides* http://www.institute.nhs.uk/images/documents/institute_documents/PDF/L02_Lean_Thinking_Slides_200 7.pdf [accessed 1 April 2008]

NHS Institute for Innovation and Improvement & Matrix Research and Consultancy (2006) *Improving the improvement system* www.institute.nhs.uk [accessed 1 April 2008]

NHS Modernisation Agency (2003) *Cancer Services Collaborative Improvement Partnership: A Quick Guide* www.modern.nhs.uk/cancer [accessed July 2004]

Nicolini, D, Powell, J, Conville, P, Martinez-Solano, L (2007) Managing knowledge in the healthcare sector. A review, *International Journal of Management Reviews*, 9 (4): 1-19

Nielsen, D M, Merry, M D, Schyve, P M, Bisognano, M (2004) Can the gurus' concepts cure healthcare? *Quality Progress*, 37 (9): Sep 25-26

Nolan, T W (1998) Understanding medical systems, *Annals of Internal Medicine*, 128 (4): 293-298

Nolan, T W, Schall, M W (1996). *Reducing delays and waiting times throughout the health care system.* Boston: Institute for Healthcare Improvement.

Nonthaleerak, P, Hendry, L C (2006) Six sigma: literature review and key future research areas *International Journal of Six Sigma and Competitive Advantage*, 2 (2): 105-161

Nuttall, P D A. (2005). *Operations management and the Theory of Constraints in the NHS*. Unpublished PhD, University of Manchester, Manchester, UK.

O'Connell, T J, Ben-Tovim, D I, McCaughan, B C, Szwarcbord, M G, McGrath, K M (2008) Health services under siege: the case for clinical process redesign, *Medical Journal of Australia*, 188 (6 Supplement): S9-S13

Ohno, T, (translator) Rosen. (1995). *Toyota Production System: Beyond large-scale Production*. New York: Productivity Press.

Oliver, N, Delbridge, R, Jones, D, Lowe, J (1994) World class manufacturing: Further evidence in the Lean production debate1, *British Journal of Management*, 5 (s1): S53-S63

Øvretveit, J (2005) Leading improvement, *Journal of Health Organization and Management*, 19 (6): 413-430

Øvretveit, J (1997) A comparison of hospital quality programmes: lessons for other services, International *Journal of Service Industry Management*, 8 (3): 220-235

Øvretveit, J, Bate, P, Cleary, P (2002) Quality collaboratives: lessons from research, *Quality and Safety in Health Care*, 11 (4): 345-351

Øvretveit, J, Gustafson, D. (2004). Evaluation of Quality Improvement Programmes. In R. Grol, R. Baker, & F. Moss (Eds.), *Quality Improvement Research*. London: BMJ Books.

Packwood, T, Pollitt, C, Roberts, S (1998) Good medicine? A case study of business process re-engineering in a hospital, *Policy and Politics*, 26 (4): 401-415

Parasuraman, A, Zeithaml, V A, Berry, L L (1988) SERVQUAL: a multiple item scale for measuring consumer perceptions of service quality, *Journal of Retailing*, 64 (1): 14-40

Parker, V A, Wubbenhorst, W, Young, G, Desai, K, Charns, M (1999) Implementing quality improvement in hospitals: the role of leadership and culture, *American Journal of Medical Quality*, 14 (1): Jan-Feb 64-69

Pauker, S G, Zane, E M, Salem, D N (2005) Creating a safer health care system: finding the constraint, *JAMA*, 294 2906-2908

Pawson, R, Greenhalgh, T, Harvey, G, Walshe, K (2005) Realist review - a new method of systematic review designed for complex policy interventions, *Journal of Health Services Research and Policy*, 10 (Supp 1): 21-34

Perneger, T (2006) Ten reasons to conduct a randomized study in quality improvement, *International Journal for Quality in Health Care*, 18 (6): 395-396

Pescod, W D T (1994) Effective use of a common problem-solving process as an integral part of TQM, *International Journal of Health Care Quality Assurance*, 7 (7): 10 -- 13

Petersen, P B (1999) Total Quality Management and the Deming approach to quality management, *Journal of Management History*, 5 (8): 468-488

Plsek, P (1999) Quality improvement methods in clinical medicine, *Pediatrics*, 103 (1): January 203-214

Pollitt, C (1993) The struggle for quality: the case of the NHS, *Policy and Politics*, 21 (3): 161-170

Proudlove, N, Gordon, K, Boaden, R (2003) Can good bed management solve the overcrowding in A&E? *Emergency Medicine Journal*, 20 (2): 149-155

Proudlove, N, Moxham, C, Boaden, R (2008) Lessons for Lean in healthcare from using Six Sigma in the NHS, *Public Money and Management*, 28 (1): 27-34

Proudlove, N C, Black, S, Fletcher, A (2007) OR and the challenge to improve the NHS: modelling for insight and improvement in inpatient flows, *Journal of the Operational Research Society*, 58 (2): 145 - 158

Proudlove, N C, Boaden, R (2006a) Information systems for supporting operational management of hospital beds in the NHS, *International Journal of Healthcare Technology and Management*, 7 (6): 474-491

Proudlove, N C, Boaden, R. (2006b). What is Six Sigma and does it matter? In K. Mendibil, & A. Shamsuddin (Eds.), *Proceedings of the European Operations Management Association* (EUROMA) Conference University of Strathclyde, Glasgow: 389-397

Pyzdek, T. (2003a). *The quality engineering handbook* (2nd ed. ed.). New York: CRC.

Pyzdek, T. (2003b). *The Six Sigma handbook*. New York: McGraw-Hill.

Radnor, Z, Boaden, R (2008). Editorial: Lean in Public Service - Panacea or Paradox?, *Public Money & Management*, 28 ed.: 3-7.

Radnor, Z, Walley, P, Stephens, A, Bucci, G (2006). *Evaluation of the Lean approach to business management and its use in the public sector.* Edinburgh: Scottish Executive, Office of Chief Researcher.

Radnor, Z J, Walley, P. (2006). Can public services be Lean? evaluating and developing the use of 'Lean' in public services. Paper presented at the Proceedings of the European Operations Management Association (EUROMA) Conference, *Glasgow* 927-935

Rahman, S (1998) Theory of Constraints: a review of the philosophy and its applications, *International Journal of Operations and Production Management*, 18 (4): 336-355

Ramanujam, R, Rousseau, D M (2006) The challenges are organizational not just clinical, *Journal of Organizational Behavior*, 27 (7): 811-827

Rand, G K (2000) Critical chain: the Theory of Constraints applied to project management, *International Journal of Project Management*, 18 (3): 173-177

Rath & Strong Management Consultants. (2005). *Rath & Strong's integrated Lean Six Sigma road map:* AON Management Consulting.

Reinertsen, J L (2006) Interview with Gary Kaplan, *Quality and safety in health care*, 15 (3): June 156-158

Reinertsen, J L, Pugh, M, Bisognano, M (2005). *Seven leadership leverage points, innovation series.* Cambridge, MA: Institute for Healthcare Improvement.

Repenning, N P, Sterman, J D (2001) Nobody ever gets credit for fixing problems that never happened: creating and sustaining process improvement, *California Management Review*, 43 (4): 64-88

Revere, L, Black, K (2003) Integrating Six Sigma with Total Quality Management: A case example for measuring medication errors, *Journal of Healthcare Management*, 48 (6): 377

Revere, L, Black, K, Huq, A (2004) Integrating Six Sigma and CQI for improving patient care, *The TQM Magazine*, 16 (2): 105-113

Ritson, N, O'Neill, M (2006) Strategic implementation: a comparison of three methodologies, *Strategic Change*, 15 (4): 187-196

Ritson, N, Waterfield, N (2005) Managing change: the Theory of Constraints in the mental health service *Strategic Change*, 14 (4): 449-458

Robert, G, McLeod, H, Ham, C (2003). *Modernising Cancer Services: an evaluation of phase I of the Cancer Services Collaborative, Research Reports.* Birmingham: University of Birmingham: Health Services Management Centre.

Robertson, P J, Seneviratne, S J (1995) Outcomes of planned organisational change in the public sector: a meta analytic comparison to the private sector, *Public Administration Review*, 55 (6): 547-558

Roth, A V (1993) World class health care, *Quality Management in Health Care*, 1 (3): 1-9

Samson, D, Terziovski, M (1999) The relationship between Total Quality Management practices and operational performance, *Journal of Operations Management*, 17 (4): 393-409

Scalise, D (2003) Six Sigma in action, *Hospitals and Health Networks*, 77 (5): May 57-61

Schein, E H. (1985). *Organisational culture and leadership*. Oxford: Jossey-Bass.

Schon, D A. (1988). *Educating the reflective practitioner. Toward a new design for teaching and learning in the professions*. San Francisco: Jossey Bass.

Schroeder, R G, Linderman, K, Liedtke, C, Choo, A S (2007) Six Sigma: *Definition and underlying theory, Journal of Operations Management*, doi:10.1016/j.jom 2007.06.007

Scorsone, E A (2008). *What are the challenges in transferring Lean thinking to government?, Public Money & Management*, 28 ed.: 61-64.

Seddon, J. (2005a). *Freedom from command and control: a better way to make the work work ... the Toyota system for service organisations* (2nd ed.). Buckingham: Vanguard Education.

Seddon, J (2005b) *Watch out for the toolheads* www.Lean-service.com [accessed 1 Feb 2005]

Sehwail, L, DeYong, C (2003) Six Sigma in health care, *International Journal of Health Care Quality Assurance*, 16 (4): i-v

Senge, P. (1990). *The fifth discipline*. New York: Doubleday.

Shaw, C D (1980) Aspects of audit, *BMJ*, 280 (6226): 1256-1258

Shewhart, W A. (1931). *Economic control of quality of manufactured product*. New York: Van Nostrand.

Short, P J, Rahmin, M A (1995) Total quality management in hospitals, *Total Quality Management*, 6 255-263

Shortell, S, Levin, D, O'Brien, J, Hughes, E (1995) Assessing the evidence on CQI: is the glass half empty or half full? *Journal of the Foundation of the American College of Healthcare Executives*, 40 (1): 4-24

Shortell, S M, Bennett, C L, Byck, G R (1998) Assessing the impact of Continuous Quality Improvement on clinical practice: what it will take to accelerate progress, *The Milbank Quarterly*, 76 (4): 593-624

Shortell, S M, O'Brien, J L, Carman, J M, Foster, R W, Hughes, E F X, Boerstler, H, O'Connor, E J (1995) Assessing the impact of Continuous Quality Improvement/Total Quality Management: concept versus implementation, *Health Services Research*, 30 (2): June 377-401

Silvester, K, Lendon, R, Bevan, H, Steyn, R, Walley, P (2004) Reducing waiting times in the NHS: is lack of capacity the problem? *Clinician in Management*, 12 (3): 105-111

Silvestro, R (1999) Positioning services along the volume-variety diagonal: The contingencies of service design, control and improvement, *International Journal of Operations and Production Management*, 19 (4): 399-420

Simmons, J C (2002) Using Six Sigma to make a difference in health care quality, *The Quality Letter*, April 2-10

Skorstad, E (1994) Lean production, conditions of work and worker commitment, *Economic and Industrial Democracy*, 15 (3): 429-455

Slack, N, Chambers, S, Johnston, R. (2007). *Operations management* (5th ed.). Harlow: Prentice Hall.

Slack, N, Chambers, S, Johnston, R, Betts, A. (2006). *Operations and process management: principles and practice for strategic impact*. Harlow: Prentice Hall.

Snee, R, Hoerl, R. (2004). *Six Sigma beyond the factory floor: Deployment strategies for financial services, healthcare and the rest of the real economy*: Prentice Hall.

Snee, R D (1990) Statistical thinking and its contribution to Total Quality, *American Statistician*, 44 (2): 116-121

Sorensen, R, Iedema, R (Eds.). (2008). *Managing clinical processes in the health services*. Sydney: Elsevier.

Spear, S (2005) Fixing healthcare from the inside, today, *Harvard Business Review*, 83 (9): September 78-91

Spear, S, Bowen, H K (1999) Decoding the DNA of the Toyota Production System, *Harvard Business Review*, 77 (5): Sep-Oct 97-106

Spear, S J (2004) Learning to lead at Toyota, *Harvard Business Review*, 82 (5): May 78-87

Speroff, T, O'Connor, G T (2004) Study designs for PDSA quality improvement research, *Quality Management in Health Care*, 13 (1): 17-32

Sprague, L G (2007) Evolution of the field of operations management, *Journal of Operations Management*, 25 (2): 219-238

Stevens, D P (2005) Three questions for QSHC, *Quality and Safety in Health Care*, 14 (1): February 1, 2005 2-3

Stevens, D P (2007) If you haven't published your work, it's time to start, *Quality and Safety in Health Care*, 16 (4): August 1, 2007 242-243

Stewart, L J, Greisler, D, Feldman, K J (2002) Measuring primary care practice performance within an integrated delivery system: A case study, *Journal of Healthcare Management*, 47 (4): 250-262

Swayne, B J (2003) First aid for health care, *Quality Digest*, December

Syrett, M, Lammiman, J. (1997). *From Leanness to fitness*. London: Cromwell Press.

Tennant, R, Mohammed, M A, Coleman, J J, Martin, U (2007) Monitoring patients using control charts: a systematic review, *International Journal of Quality in Health Care*, 19 (4): August 1, 2007 187-194

Thomerson, L D. (2001). Journey for excellence: Kentucky's Commonwealth Health Corporation adopts Six Sigma approach. Paper presented at the Annual Quality Congress, *Charlotte*, NC, May 152-156

Thomerson, L D. (2002). Six Sigma intensified - is 99% good enough...? Paper presented at the Annual Quality Congress, *Denver*, CO, May 297-307

Thompson, D N, Wolf, G A, Spear, S J (2003) Driving improvement in patient care: lessons from Toyota, *Journal of Nursing Administration*, 33 (11): 585-595

Thompson, M, Nussbaum, R (2000) An HMO survey on mass customization of healthcare delivery for women, *Women's Health Issues*, 10 (1): 10-19

Thomson, P, Lewis, M (2002) UVa Compliance department uses Six Sigma model to improve performance, *Journal of Healthcare Compliance*, 4 (5): 5

Thor, J, Lundberg, J, Ask, J, Olsson, J A, Carli, C, Pukk Harenstam, K, Brommels, M (2007) Application of statistical process control in healthcare improvement: systematic review, *Quality and Safety in Health Care*, 16 387-399

Umble, M, Umble, E J (2006) Utilizing buffer management to improve performance in a healthcare environment, *European Journal of Operational Research*, 174 1060–1075

van den Heuvel, J, Does, R J M M, Verver, J P S (2005) Six Sigma in healthcare: lessons learned from a hospital *International Journal of Six Sigma and Competitive Advantage* 1(4): 380-388

Vinzant, J C, Vinzant, D H (1999) Strategic management spin-offs of the Deming approach, *Journal of Management History*, 5 (8): 516 - 531

Voss, C A (1995) Operations management - from Taylor to Toyota - and beyond? *British Journal of Management*, 6 (special issue): S17-S29

Walley, P (2003a) Designing the accident and emergency system: lessons from manufacturing, *Emergency Medicine Journal*, 20 (2): March 1, 2003 126-130

Walley, P, Silvester, K, Mountford, S (2006a) Healthcare process improvement decisions: a systems perspective, *International Journal of Healthcare and Quality Assurance*, 19 (1): 93-104

Walley, P, Silvester, K, Steyn, R, Conway, J B (2006b) Managing variation in demand: lessons from the UK National Health Service, *Journal of Healthcare Management*, 51 (5): 309-325

Walshe, K (2007) Understanding what works - and why - in quality improvement: the need for theory-driven evaluation, *International Journal of Quality in Health Care*, 19 (2): April 1, 2007 57-59

Webb, J. (1995). Quality management and the management of quality. In A. Wilkinson, & H. Willmott (Eds.), *Making Quality Critical*. London: Routledge.

Wenger, E, Snyder, W M (2000) Communities of practice: the organisational frontier, *Harvard Business Review*, 78 (1): Jan/Feb 139

Westwood, N, James-Moore, M, Cooke, M (2007). *Going Lean in the NHS*: NHS Institute for Innovation and Improvement/Warwick University.

Westwood, N, Silvester, K (2007) Eliminate NHS losses by adding Lean and some Six Sigma, *Operations Management*, 33 (5): 26-30

White, R E, Pearson, J N, Wilson, J R (1999) JIT Manufacturing: A survey of implementations in small and large U.S. manufacturers, *Management Science*, 45 (1): Jan 1-15

Wilkinson, A (1992) The other side of quality: soft issues and the human resource dimension, *Total Quality Management*, 3 (3): 323-329

Wilkinson, A, Willmott, H (Eds.). (1995). *Making quality critical*. London: Routledge.

Wilkinson, A J, Brown, A. (2003). Managing human resources for quality management. In B. G. Dale (Ed.), *Managing Quality*. Oxford: Blackwell: 177-202

Wilson, T, Berwick, D M, Cleary, P D (2003) What do collaborative improvement projects do? Experience from seven countries, *Joint Commission Journal on Quality and Safety*, 29 (2): 85-93

Womack, D E, Flowers, S (1999) Improving system performance: A case study in the application of the Theory of Constraints, *Journal of Healthcare Management*, 44 (5): Sep/Oct 397

Womack, J, Jones, D T, Roos, D. (1990). *The machine that changed the world*. New York: Rawson Associates.

Womack, J P. (2004). An action plan for Lean services. Paper presented at the Lean Service Summit, *Amsterdam*, June 23-24

Womack, J P, Jones, D T. (1996). *Lean thinking*. London: Simon and Schuster.

Wright, A (1997) Public service quality: Lessons not learned, *Total Quality Management*, 8 (5): October 313-321

Wright, J, King, R. (2006). *We all fall down*. Great Barrington, MA: North River Press.

Young, T, Brailsford, S, Connell, C, Davies, R, Harper, P, Klein, J H (2004) Using industrial processes to improve patient care, *BMJ*, 328 (7432): January 17, 2004 162-164

Zbabada, C, Rivers, P A, Munchus, G (1998) Obstacles to the application of TQM in healthcare organisations, *Total Quality Management*, 9 (1): 57-67

Zimmerman, R S (2004) Hospital capacity, productivity and patient safety - it all flows together, *Frontiers of Health Services Management*, 20 (4): Summer 33-38

APPENDIX 1 - The authors of the report

All the authors are members of staff at Manchester Business School. Full details of their work and publications can be found by searching for their name at www.mbs.ac.uk

Ruth Boaden | Ruth is Professor of Service Operations Management and Deputy Director of the Greater Manchester Collaboration for Leadership in Applied Health Research and Care (CLAHRC). Her research interests cover a wide range of areas within health services management and include work in electronic health records, re-engineering, operating theatre management and scheduling, patient safety, the management of Emergency Admissions, bed management and chronic disease management. Her main areas of interest are in quality and improvement and the use of industrial methods within the NHS, as well as the implementation of new approaches. She has a focus on knowledge transfer arising from high quality research, to ensure that the findings are accessible and applicable to practice. She has published widely in these areas as well as in the areas of IT implementation and quality management. She set up and directed the Leadership through Effective People Management programme for the NHS, which was run in partnership with PricewaterhouseCoopers from 2001-2006 and provided for directors and deputies from across the NHS.

Gill Harvey | Gill is a senior lecturer in healthcare and public sector management. She has a professional background in nursing and prior to taking up post at MBS (in August 2003), Gill had worked for nine years as the director of the Royal College of Nursing's Quality Improvement Programme. In this post, she was responsible for leading the RCN's work on clinical guidelines, audit, clinical governance and healthcare quality improvement and was involved in a wide range of educational, research, development and policy-focused activities. Gill's own research interests are particularly focused on evaluative research around issues of implementation and facilitating quality improvement in practice. Current research activities include projects on organisational failure and turnaround, knowledge translation and utilisation and evaluating improvement initiatives in the NHS.

Whilst working at the RCN, Gill was responsible for establishing and leading the NICE funded National Collaborating Centre for Nursing and Supportive Care. She is a past Co-Chair of the European Forum for Quality Improvement in Health Care and for several years was an associate editor of the Quality and Safety in Healthcare journal.

Nathan Proudlove	Nathan is a senior lecturer in operational research. He has worked on health management issues since the mid-1990s. Nathan's particular interests are operation management and flow issues such as capacity and demand, forecasting, bed management, and process improvement. He has worked with many hospital trusts and with the NHS Modernisation Agency, in particular Intensive Support Teams, the Innovation and Knowledge Group, and the Emergency Care Strategy Team. He also has links with the NHS in Wales and Northern Ireland. He has published in a range of academic and practitioner journals in the healthcare field, including the Health Service Journal, the International Journal of Healthcare Technology and Management, the Emergency Medicine Journal, the British Journal of Healthcare Computing and Information Management, and the Journal of Health Organisation and Management. He has also contributed guidance to the National Electronic Library for Health, and advice on healthcare issues to the National Audit Office and Prime Minister's Delivery Unit.
Claire Moxham	Claire is a lecturer in the decision sciences and operations management group. Her background is in process improvement and she has held managerial positions in the textile and caravan manufacturing industries. Prior to her appointment at MBS Claire spent three years as a Voluntary Service Overseas volunteer lecturing in operations management in Ethiopia. Claire joined MBS in September 2003 and teaches operations and quality management at undergraduate, postgraduate and post-experience levels. Her areas of expertise include performance measurement, process improvement, and the application of industrial management techniques to the public and voluntary sectors.